ILLUSTRATIONS

OF

THE BRITISH FLORA

ILLUSTRATIONS
of
THE BRITISH FLORA

A SERIES OF

WOOD ENGRAVINGS, WITH DISSECTIONS

OF

BRITISH PLANTS

Drawn by
W. H. FITCH, F.L.S.
with additions by
W. G. SMITH, F.L.S.
AND OTHERS

Forming an illustrated companion to
Bentham's Handbook of The British Flora
and other Floras.

FIFTH REVISED EDITION
(*Fifth Reprint*)

L. REEVE & CO., LTD.
LLOYDS BANK BUILDINGS, BANK ST., ASHFORD, KENT
1949

By GEORGE BENTHAM, F.R.S., and Sir J. D. HOOKER, C.B., G.C.S.I., F.R.S.

HANDBOOK OF THE BRITISH FLORA; a description of the Flowering Plants and Ferns indigenous to, or naturalized in, the British Isles. With an introduction on the Outlines of Botany in special reference to local Floras, and an analytical Key to the Families and anomalous Genera for students and beginners. Seventh revised edition, edited by A. B. Rendle, M.A., D.Sc., F.R.S. pp. lxi + 606. Price 17s. 6d. net.

By R. W. BUTCHER, B.Sc., F.L.S., and F. E. STRUDWICK, Nat. Sc. Tripos (Cantab.), M.A. (Dublin).

FURTHER ILLUSTRATIONS OF BRITISH PLANTS. Forming a more complete British Flora together with Bentham's Handbook and Illustrations. 485 new figures with descriptions. Crown 8vo. Price 17s. 6d. net.

By J. ADAMS, M.A. (Cantab.), Economic Botanist, Ottawa, Canada.

A STUDENTS' ILLUSTRATED IRISH FLORA; being a guide to the Indigenous Seed-Plants of Ireland. Illustration and particulars of distribution of each plant. Additional Chapters on Classification, Relation to Environment, Topographical Distribution. Lists of Poisonous Plants and Lists of English and Irish Names. Crown 8vo. pp. viii + 343. 578 Illustrations and Outline Map of Ireland. Price 17s. 6d. net.

PREFACE.

THE illustrations contained in this volume were drawn, with the few exceptions presently referred to, by W. H. Fitch, F.L.S., for the original illustrated edition of Bentham's " Handbook of the British Flora." Since that edition was exhausted they have been issued separately, forming a companion volume to the " Handbook " and to other general, county and local Floras. Additional drawings by W. G. Smith, F.L.S., and others, have been incorporated from time to time illustrating additions to the Flora.

The arrangement in the present edition follows that of the latest edition of Bentham's " Handbook."

The " Arrangement of Families," with some of their distinguishing characters, is reproduced from the " Handbook," and this is preceded by descriptions of the main divisions of classification. Those who have not made a previous study of systematic botany may obtain from these a general conception of the main principles upon which the arrangement of the Families is based. But until a knowledge of the subject is acquired by practical observation, the " Analytical Key to the Families and anomalous genera," also reproduced from the " Handbook," will be of more service in identifying the Families to which plants are assigned, for the reason that this " Analytical Key " is constructed from the more easily observed characters, which are not necessarily those which determine the systematic arrangement.

In the body of the work the scientific names of the plants as adopted in the latest edition of the " Handbook " are given first in larger type. To these are added in small type the names used in the previous edition of the " Handbook " in cases where alteration has been necessary.

The English names are also added to each illustration, and are followed by an indication of the colour of the flower except where it is always white, cream, or only tinged with colour, or green and inconspicuous.

B. signifies Blue.	Pk. signifies Pink.
Br. „ Brown.	R. „ Red, Orange, Scarlet or
G. „ Green.	Crimson.
Li. „ Lilac.	W. „ White.
P. „ Purple.	Y. „ Yellow.

Although the illustrations are necessarily small and not intended to be coloured, many persons have found it of interest to do so, perhaps as a record of their observation and identification of the plants themselves; a paper suitable for colouring has therefore been used.

July, 1924.

CLASSIFICATION.

TABLE OF CLASSES.

1. **ANGIOSPERMS.**   Seeds enclosed within a fruit.

CLASS I.—DICOTYLEDONS.

Stem, when perennial, consisting of a pith in the centre, of one or more concentric circles containing woody tissue, and of bark on the outside.   Seeds with two cotyledons, the young stem in germination proceeding from between the two lobes of the embryo, or from the notch in its summit.

These characters are all that can be said to be constant to separate *Dicotyledons* from *Monocotyledons*.   They are, however, in most cases very difficult to observe, and yet the distinction is essential, for these two great classes have each their peculiar aspect, which, after a very little practice, the botanist will in most cases recognise at a glance.   The nerves of the leaves are branched and netted, and the parts of the flower are usually in fours or fives (*see* the " Handbook," p. 1).   Families i.–lxxiii.

CLASS II.—MONOCOTYLEDONS.

Stem not distinguishable into pith, wood, and bark, but consisting of bundles of woody fibres, irregularly imbedded in cellular tissue.   Seeds with one cotyledon, the embryo undivided, the young stem being developed from a sheath-like cavity on one side.

Besides these positive characters, *Monocotyledons* may be generally known by their simple, entire, alternate or radical leaves, with simple parallel veins, the base usually encircling or sheathing the stem or the base of the next leaf ; and the parts of the flower are most frequently in threes, the calyx and corolla, when present, being generally similar in appearance, forming a single perianth of 6 parts (*see* the " Handbook," p. 433).

Families lxxv.–lxxxix.

2. **GYMNOSPERMS.**   Seeds not enclosed within a fruit.

Family lxxiv.

3. **VASCULAR CRYPTOGAMS.**

No real flowers, that is, neither stamens, nor pistils, nor true seeds, the fructification consisting of minute granules, called *Spores*, variously enclosed in *Spore-cases* (*sporangia*).   The few British *Cryptogams* which are included in the present volume have all of them roots, and stems or rootstocks, as in flowering plants, and in a few the leaves are somewhat similar (*see* the " Handbook," p. 565).   Families xc.–xcix.

Sub-Classes of Class I. **DICOTYLEDONS.**

Sub-class 1. **Thalamiflorae.** — Petals distinct from the calyx, and from each other, seldom wanting. Stamens usually hypogynous, or nearly so (for exceptions *see* p. ix). Families i–xxi

Sub-class 2. **Calyciflorae.** — Petals usually distinct, and stamens perigynous or epigynous (for exceptions *see* p. xi). Families xxii–xxxviii

Sub-class 3. **Monopetalae.** — Petals united (at least at the base) into a single corolla (for exceptions *see* p. xii). Families xxxix–lx

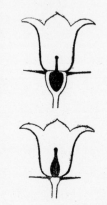

Sub-class 4. **Monochlamydeae.** — Perianth really or apparently simple or none (for exceptions *see* p. xiv). Families lxi–lxxiv

FAMILIES

(NATURAL ORDERS)

ARRANGEMENT OF THE FAMILIES IN THE PRESENT WORK.

THE following recapitulation of the Families represented in the British Isles is merely intended as a table of contents, showing the order in which the families follow each other in the present work ; at the same time attention is called to one or two of the most striking, the most important, or the easiest observed features of each one. These characters are, however, general, not always without exception, and sometimes specially applicable to British genera only.

ANGIOSPERMS.

CLASS I.—DICOTYLEDONS.

In the germination of the seed the plumule arises between two (rarely more) lobes or cotyledons of the embryo, or from a terminal notch. The vascular tissue of the stem forms a ring or rings between the bark and pith. The nerves of the leaf are branched and netted (see also *Arum, Tamus,* and *Paris* in Monocotyledons). The parts of the flower are usually in fours or fives.

Sub-class 1. **Thalamifloræ.**—Petals distinct from the calyx, and from each other, seldom wanting. Stamens usually hypogynous, or nearly so. *Exceptions.*—The calyx or corolla is absent in some *Ranunculaceæ, Cruciferæ, Violaceæ, Caryophyllaceæ.* The petals cohere more or less in some *Fumariaceæ, Polygalaceæ, Portulacaceæ, Tamaricaceæ, Malvaceæ.* The stamens are epigynous or perigynous in *Nymphæaceæ* and some *Caryophyllaceæ.*

* *Ovary apocarpous.*

I. RANUNCULACEÆ (figs. 1–32). Petals definite. Stamens indefinite.

II. BERBERIDACEÆ (fig. 33). Perianth and stamens in twos or threes, or their multiples. Anthers opening by recurved valves.

III. NYMPHÆACEÆ (figs. 34–5). Aquatic plants with indefinite petals and stamens, the inner petals passing gradually into the outer stamens.

** *Ovary syncarpous. Placentas parietal (except in* Polygaleæ).

IV. PAPAVERACEÆ (figs. 36–44). Perianth regular, in twos or fours. Stamens indefinite.

V. FUMARIACEÆ (figs. 45–7). Perianth very irregular, in twos or fours. Stamens 6, in two sets.

VI. CRUCIFERÆ (figs. 48–113). Sepals and petals 4 each. Stamens 6, of which 2 shorter.

VII. RESEDACEÆ (figs. 114–6). Petals small, unequal, some divided. Stamens few, but indefinite. Capsule open at the top before it is ripe.

VIII. CISTACEÆ (figs. 117–20). Sepals 3, equal, or with additional small ones. Petals 5, regular. Stamens indefinite.

IX. VIOLACEÆ (figs. 121–6). Stamens 5 ; the anthers on the inner face of very short broad filaments, usually united in a ring. Capsule 3-valved.

X. POLYGALACEÆ (fig. 127). Perianth very irregular. Stamens 8, in two parcels ; petals united with them. Capsule 2-celled.

XI. FRANKENIACEÆ (fig. 128). As in Caryophyllaceæ, except the parietal placentas.

*** *Ovary syncarpous. Placentas axile.*

XII. CARYOPHYLLACEÆ (figs. 129–73). Leaves opposite, entire. Flowers regular. Stamens definite. Capsule 1-celled, with a free-central placenta.

XIII. PORTULACACEÆ (figs. 174–5). As in Caryophyllaceæ, but only 2 sepals and 5 or more petals.

XIV. TAMARICACEÆ (fig. 176). Shrubs with alternate green scale-like leaves. Flowers regular. Capsule 1-celled. Seeds with a tuft of wool.

XV. ELATINACEÆ (figs. 177–8). As in Caryophyllaceæ, but the capsule divided into cells.

XVI. HYPERICACEÆ (figs. 179–89). Leaves opposite. Flowers regular. Sepals imbricate. Stamens indefinite, in 3 or 5 clusters or bundles.

XVII. LINACEÆ (figs. 190–4). Leaves entire. Petals convolute, distinct. Stamens definite. Capsule separating into carpels without leaving a central axis.

XVIII. MALVACEÆ (figs. 195–200). Sepals valvate. Petals convolute, adhering at the base to the staminal tube. Stamens indefinite, monadelphous, with 1-celled anthers.

XIX. TILIACEÆ (fig. 201). Trees. Sepals valvate. Petals free. Stamens indefinite.

XX. GERANIACEÆ (figs. 202–20). Petals convolute or very

irregular. Stamens definite. Capsule with several cells and lobes round a persistent central axis.

XXI. ACERACEÆ (figs. 221–2). Trees. Leaves opposite. Stamens definite, but seldom isomerous. Fruit separating into 2 (rarely 3) winged nuts.

Sub-class 2. **Calyciflora.**—Petals usually distinct, and stamens perigynous or epigynous. *Exceptions.*—The petals are absent in some *Rosaceæ, Onagraceæ, Lythraceæ, Saxifragaceæ, Haloragaceæ,* and *Loranthaceæ.* The petals cohere more or less in some *Aquifoliaceæ, Cucurbitaceæ* and *Crassulaceæ.* The stamens are hypogynous in some *Saxifragaceæ,* and in *Droraceæ,* and are epipetalous in some *Crassulaceæ.*

* *Stamens and petals mostly perigynous (except in* Crassulaceæ, Cucurbitaceæ, *and* Ribesiaceæ).

XXII. AQUIFOLIACEÆ (fig. 223). Shrubs or trees with small flowers. Petals shortly united at the base. Stamens alternating with them. No disk. Ovary syncarpous, free.

XXIII. CELASTRACEÆ (fig. 224). Shrubs or trees, with small regular green flowers. Stamens alternating with the petals, on a disk lining the base of the calyx.

XXIV. RHAMNACEÆ (figs. 225–6). As in Celastraceæ, but the stamens are opposite the small concave or scale-like petals.

XXV. PAPILIONACEÆ, a tribe of LEGUMINOSÆ (figs. 227–97). Flowers very irregular, *papilionaceous.* Stamens 10, all, or 9 of them, combined. Ovary of one carpel.

XXVI. ROSACEÆ (figs. 298–341). Flowers regular. Stamens indefinite. Ovary (at least when young) apocarpous.

XXVII. ONAGRACEÆ (figs. 342–54). Perianth in twos or fours. Stamens definite. Ovary inferior. One style.

XXVIII. LYTHRACEÆ (figs. 355–7). Stamens usually definite, inserted with the petals at the top of the calyx-tube. Ovary syncarpous within the base of the tube. One style. Lower leaves opposite.

XXIX. CUCURBITACEÆ (fig. 358). Climbers with tendrils. Flowers unisexual. Ovary inferior.

XXX. CRASSULACEÆ (figs. 359–71). Leaves succulent. Sepals, petals, stamens of one or two rows, and free carpels, all isomerous.

XXXI. RIBESIACEÆ (figs. 372–5). Shrubs. Flowers regular. Stamens definite. Ovary inferior. Placentas parietal. One style.

XXXII. SAXIFRAGACEÆ (figs. 376–91). Flowers regular. Stamens definite. Ovary syncarpous at the base, but a separate style for each carpel.

XXXIII. DROSERACEÆ (figs. 392–4). Herbs with radical leaves covered with long glandular hairs. Flowers regular. Stamens definite. Placentas parietal. Styles distinct.

XXXIV. HALORAGACEÆ (figs. 395–7). Aquatic herbs with very small flowers. Calyx-lobes and petals 4, 2, or none. Stamens definite. Ovary inferior. Styles or stigmas distinct.

** *Petals and stamens epigynous (round an epigynous disk).*

XXXV. UMBELLIFERÆ (figs. 398–456). Leaves alternate. Fruit dry, separating from the axis into seed-like carpels.

XXXVI. ARALIACEÆ (fig. 457). Leaves alternate. Fruit succulent. Carpels often more than 2, and not separating.

XXXVII. LORANTHACEÆ (fig. 458). Parasites. Stamens on, or opposite to the petals. Leaves usually opposite. Ovary 1-celled.

XXXVIII. CORNACEÆ (figs. 459–60). Leaves usually opposite. Stamens alternate with the petals. Style one.

Sub-class 3. **Monopetalæ.**—Petals united (at least at the base) into a single corolla. The petals are absent in some *Primulaceæ* and *Oleaceæ*, and are free in some *Ericaceæ* and *Plumbaginaceæ*.

(1) *Corolla epigynous, bearing the stamens.*

XXXIX. CAPRIFOLIACEÆ (figs. 461–9). Leaves opposite. No stipules. Ovary 2- or more-celled.

XL. STELLATÆ, a tribe of RUBIACEÆ (figs. 470–83). Stipules like the leaves in appearance, and forming whorls with them round the stem. Ovary 2-celled, with 1 seed in each cell.

XLI. VALERIANACEÆ (figs. 484–91). Stamens fewer than the lobes of the corolla. Ovary and fruit 1-seeded.

XLII. DIPSACACEÆ (figs. 492–6). Florets in compact heads or spikes. Stamens isomerous. Anthers free. Ovary and fruit 1-seeded.

XLIII. COMPOSITÆ (figs. 497–611). Florets in compact heads. Stamens isomerous. Anthers united in a ring round the style. Ovary and fruit 1-seeded.

(2) *Stamens free from the corolla.*

XLIV. CAMPANULACEÆ (figs. 612–25). Herbs. Stamens as many as the corolla-lobes. Anthers opening longitudinally.

XLV. ERICACEÆ (figs. 626–48). Shrubs. Stamens usually twice as many as the corolla-lobes. Anthers opening in pores or cross-valves.

(3) *Corolla hypogynous, bearing the stamens.*

     * *Placenta free-central.*

    XLVI. PRIMULACEÆ (figs. 649–63). Stamens isomerous and opposite the corolla-lobes.

    XLVII. LENTIBULARIACEÆ (figs. 664–9). Corolla very irregular. Stamens fewer than the lobes, and alternate with them.

    ** *Placentas parietal, or in the axial angle of the cells.*

       (*a*) *Corolla regular, or nearly so.*

    XLVIII. OLEACEÆ (figs. 670–1). Trees or shrubs. Stamens 2, alternating with the 2 ovary-cells, and having no constant relation to the corolla-lobes.

    XLIX. APOCYNACEÆ (figs. 672–3). Corolla contorted. Stamens isomerous. Ovary of 2 carpels, usually distinct, whilst the styles are united at the top.

    L. GENTIANACEÆ (figs. 674–84). Bitter plants. Corolla contorted. Stamens isomerous. Placentas parietal, rarely meeting in the axis.

    LI. POLEMONIACEÆ (fig. 685). Corolla contorted. Stamens isomerous. Ovary 3-celled, with several seeds.

    LII. CONVOLVULACEÆ (figs. 686–91). Corolla plaited. Stamens isomerous. Ovary 2- or 3-celled, with 2 (rarely 1) ovules in each, often separated by an additional false partition.

    LIII. BORAGINACEÆ (figs. 692–712). Stamens isomerous. Ovary 2- or 4-lobed, with one ovule in each lobe.

    LIV. SOLANACEÆ (figs. 713–7). Stamens isomerous. Corolla plaited or imbricate. Ovary 2-celled, with several ovules in each cell.

       (*b*) *Corolla irregular. Stamens* 1 *less or* 3 *less than the lobes.*

    LV. OROBANCHACEÆ (figs. 718–25). Leafless parasites. Placentas parietal, or rarely meeting in the axis.

    LVI. SCROPHULARIACEÆ (figs. 726–76). Ovary 2-celled, with several ovules in each cell.

    LVII. LABIATÆ (figs. 777–821). Ovary 4-lobed, with 1 ovule in each lobe.

    LVIII. VERBENACEÆ (fig. 822). Ovary entire, 2- or 4-celled, with 1 ovule in each cell.

    *** *Anomalous families.*

    LIX. PLUMBAGINACEÆ (figs. 823–7). Ovary with 1 cell and ovule, but several styles.

    XL. PLANTAGINACEÆ (figs. 828–33). Corolla scarious. Stamen isomerous.

Sub-class 4.   **Monochlamydeæ.**—Perianth really or apparently simple or none. *Exceptions.*—Petals are present in some *Illecebraceæ*.

LXI. ILLECEBRACEÆ (figs. 834–8). Perianth small, rarely double. Ovary with 1 cell and ovule, but 2 or 3 styles or stigmas. Leaves usually opposite, with scarious stipules.

LXII. CHENOPODIACEÆ (figs. 839–57). Perianth small ; stamens opposite to its lobes. Ovary with 1 cell and ovule, but 2 or more styles or stigmas. No stipules.

LXIII. POLYGONACEÆ (figs. 858–79). Perianth small. Ovary with 1 cell and ovule, but 2 or more styles or stigmas. Stipules sheathing.

LXIV. THYMELEACEÆ (figs. 880–1). Stamens inserted in the tube of the perianth, and usually double the number of its lobes. Ovary free, with 1 pendulous ovule. One style.

LXV. ELÆAGNACEÆ (fig. 882). Shrubs or trees, with scurfy leaves. Flowers mostly unisexual. Ovary free in the bottom of the perianth-tube, with 1 erect ovule.

LXVI. SANTALACEÆ (fig. 883). Perianth-lobes valvate. Ovary inferior, 1-celled, with 2 or 4 pendulous ovules. Spike simple.

LXVII. ARISTOLOCHIACEÆ (fig. 884). Perianth irregular, or 3-lobed. Stamens 6 or 12. Ovary inferior, 3- or 6-celled, with numerous ovules.

LXVIII. EUPHORBIACEÆ (figs. 885–99). Flowers unisexual. Fruit separating into 3 (rarely 2 or more) carpels, leaving a persistent axis, each carpel containing 1 or 2 pendulous seeds.

LXIX. EMPETRACEÆ (fig. 900). Differs from Euphorbiaceæ in the ovules and seeds erect.

LXX. CERATOPHYLLUM and CALLITRICHE (figs. 901–2). Anomalous aquatic genera. Perianth none. Ovary with 1 or 4 cells, and 1 seed in each.

LXXI. URTICACEÆ (figs. 903–7). Flowers unisexual, small and green. Stamens opposite the perianth-divisions (usually 4) Ovary free, with a single ovule, and 2 (rarely 1) styles or stigmas.

LXXII. ULMACEÆ (figs. 908–9). Trees. Flowers often bisexual, the stamens opposite the lobes. Ovary free, 2-celled, with 1 erect ovule in each cell.

LXXIII. AMENTACEÆ (figs. 910–35). Trees or shrubs. Flowers unisexual, the males in catkins with an imperfect perianth, or none at all. Fruit of the females 1-celled.

GYMNOSPERMS.

LXXIV. CONIFERÆ (figs. 936–8). Trees or shrubs with stiff or scale-like leaves. Flowers unisexual, the males in catkins without perianth. Ovules and seeds in the females not enclosed in an ovary or pericarp.

ANGIOSPERMS.

CLASS II.—MONOCOTYLEDONS.

In germination the plumule is developed from a sheath-like cavity on one side of the embryo. The vascular tissue of the stem occurs in scattered bundles amongst the cellular. The nerves of the leaves are more or less parallel (except in *Araceæ*, *Dioscoreaceæ*, *Paris*, and in some *Liliaceæ*). The parts of the flower are usually in twos or threes.

* *Perianth none, or of 4 small sepals or bracts.*

LXXV. TYPHACEÆ (figs. 939–43). Flowers unisexual, inter-mixed with bracts in dense heads or spikes. Fruit a dry nut.

LXXVI. ARACEÆ (figs. 944–5). Flowers unisexual, often intermixed with bracts in dense heads or spikes, mostly in a spathe. Fruits usually succulent.

LXXVII. LEMNACEÆ (figs. 946–50). No distinct stem Flowers (very scarce) on the edge of the small leaf-like floating fronds.

LXXVIII. NAIADACEÆ (figs. 951–71). Floating or submerged plants. Flowers distinct or in loose spikes. Stamens 1, 2, or 4. Ovaries 1, 2, or 4.

** *Perianth wholly or partially petal-like. Ovary apocarpous.*

LXXIX. ALISMACEÆ (figs. 972–7) ; the only British family of the group.

*** *Perianth wholly or partially petal-like. Ovary inferior.*

LXXX. HYDROCHARIDACEÆ (figs. 978–80). Floating or sub-merged plants. Flowers usually unisexual. Perianth regular, with a slender tube.

LXXXI. ORCHIDACEÆ (figs. 981–1016). Perianth very irregu-lar. Anther 2-celled, combined with the style in an axile column.

LXXXII. IRIDACEÆ (1017–23). Like Amaryllidaceæ, but stamens 3. Leaves often in two opposite rows.

LXXXIII. AMARYLLIDACEÆ (figs. 1024–7). Terrestrial plants. Perianth of 6 divisions. Stamens 6.

LXXXIV. DIOSCOREACEÆ (fig. 1028). Twining plants. Flowers unisexual. Perianth regular, of 6 divisions.

**** *Perianth regular. Ovary syncarpous, superior.*

LXXXV. LILIACEÆ (figs. 1029–59). Perianth petal-like.

LXXXVI. JUNCACEÆ (figs. 1060–81). Perianth stiff, or calyx-like. Capsule 3-celled, with several seeds, or 1 erect seed in each cell.

LXXXVII. ERIOCAULACEÆ (fig. 1082). Perianth calyx-like. Flowers unisexual. Ovary with 1 pendulous ovule in each cell.

***** *Perianth rudimentary or none, replaced by chaffy scales or bracts enclosing the flowers.*

LXXXVIII. CYPERACEÆ (figs. 1083–1157). Leaf-sheaths entire. Each flower in the axil of one bract.

LXXXIX. GRAMINEÆ (figs. 1158–1257). Leaf-sheaths split open opposite the blade. Each flower enclosed in two bracts.

VASCULAR CRYPTOGAMS.

No true flowers ; that is, no stamens or pistils.

XC. LYCOPODIACEÆ (figs. 1258–62). Spores of one form only, in closed capsules (sporangia) in the axils of the leaves, or of the bracts of a terminal spike.

XCI. SELAGINELLACEÆ (fig. 1263). Spores of two forms, in sporangia in the axils of the leaves, or of the bracts of a spike.

XCII. ISOETACEÆ (figs. 1264–5). Spores of two forms in sporangia partially enclosed in the base of the narrow leaves which are borne on a depressed corm.

XCIII. MARSILEACEÆ (fig. 1266). Spores of two forms in small sporangia enclosed in globular or ovoid involucres placed on the rootstock.

XCIV. SALVINIACEÆ (fig. 1267). Small floating plants with sporangia of two forms borne on the submerged segments of the leaves in groups which are surrounded by a globular indusium.

XCV. EQUISETACEÆ (figs. 1268–77). Stems jointed, with whorled branches. Sporangia borne under peltate scales, in terminal heads or spikes.

FILICES (figs. 1278–1315). Spores minute of one form in sporangia clustered on the back or margin of the fronds, or on a branch of the frond.

XCVI. OPHIOGLOSSACEÆ (figs. 1278–9).

XCVII. OSMUNDACEÆ (fig. 1280).

XCVIII. POLYPODIACEÆ (figs. 1281–1312).

XCIX. HYMENOPHYLLACEÆ (figs. 1313–5).

ANALYTICAL KEY TO THE FAMILIES AND ANOMALOUS GENERA OF THE BRITISH FLORA

The heads of division adopted in the following Key are necessarily artificial, being solely intended to assist the beginner in finding out the name of his plant, and its place in the system, like the letters of the alphabet in an index. They are not classes or groups of Families, for the same Family will be found repeated under different heads. At the same time, it has been the endeavour so to frame them as to call the student's attention to some of the most prominent characters of the great natural divisions.

I. FLOWERING PLANTS.

1 { Flowers compound, consisting of several florets in a common involucre, without separate calyces. Anthers united in a cylinder round the style 2
Flowers distinct, or if in a head, having the anthers free . . 3

2 { Ovary and fruit containing a single seed, and appearing like a seed under the floret . . . . . COMPOSITÆ (p. 125).
Ovary and fruit 2-celled, with several seeds . JASIONE (p. 154).

3 { Perianth double, consisting of a calyx (sometimes reduced to a scarcely prominent ring) and a corolla 4
Perianth single (its segments all calyx-like, or all petal-like) or none 85

4 { Corolla consisting of several distinct petals 5
Corolla of one piece, the petals united, at least at the base . 8

5 { Ovary free, within or above the petals 6
Ovary inferior, and below the petals 46

6 { Ovaries several in the same flower, the carpels distinct or deeply divided . . . .
Ovary solitary (simple or compound) entire or slightly divided . 7

7 { Corolla regular, the petals equal and similar to each other . 15
Corolla irregular 41

8 { Ovary inferior, below the insertion of the corolla . . . 51
Ovary superior or free, within the tube or base of the corolla . 57

Polypetals with several free, distinct ovaries or carpels.

9 { Stamens united in a ring or column enclosing the style. Ovaries in a ring round the axis 10
Stamens free. Ovaries quite free, each with a distinct style or stigma, without a central axis 11

10 { Stamens 5 or 10, shortly united at the base GERANIACEÆ (p. 51).
Stamens indefinite, united in a column . MALVACEÆ (p. 49).

11 { Stamens definite in number (as many, twice, or thrice as many as the petals) 12
Stamens indefinite (many or rarely few) 13

12 { Leaves fleshy. Sepals and petals 4 or more CRASSULACEÆ (p. 90).
Aquatic plants not fleshy. Sepals and petals 3 each.
ALISMACEÆ (p. 242).

13 { Leaves without stipules. Stamens hypogynous . . 14
Leaves with stipules. Stamens perigynous . ROSACEÆ (p. 75).

14 { Sepals or petals or both 4 or more . . RANUNCULACEÆ (p. 1).
Sepals and petals 3 each . . . . ALISMACEÆ (p. 242).

Regular Polypetals with one free, simple, or compound ovary.

15 { More than 10 stamens 16
10 stamens or fewer 22

16 { Calyx of 2 distinct sepals. Petals 4 . PAPAVERACEÆ (p. 10).
Calyx of one piece, with 5 or more teeth. Petals 5 or 6. Stamens about 12 17
Calyx of 3 to 5 sepals or lobes. Petals 5. Stamens numerous . 18
Calyx of several sepals. Petals and stamens numerous. Aquatic plants . . . . NYMPHÆACEÆ (p. 9).

17 { Petals distinct. Ovary sessile . . . LYTHRUM (p. 89).
Apparent petals really appendages to the involucre. Ovary apparently stalked . . . . . EUPHORBIA (p. 221)

B

18 Leaves opposite . . . 19
Leaves alternate . . . 20

19 Sepals 3, with or without 2 small outer ones. Style simple. CISTACEÆ (p. 30).
Sepals 5, nearly equal. Styles 3 or 5, distinct HYPERICACEÆ (p. 45).
Trees or shrubs. Stamens free . . . 21

20 Herbs. Stamens free . . . ACTÆA (p. 8).
Herbs or undershrubs. Stamens united in a column round the pistil . . . MALVACEÆ (p. 49).

21 Petals and stamens hypogynous. Flower-stalk winged by an oblong bract . . . TILIACEÆ (p. 50).
Petals and stamens perigynous. Flower-stalk not winged. ROSACEÆ (p. 75).

22 Leaves opposite . . . 23
Leaves alternate, or radical, or none . . . 30

23 Trees or shrubs . . . 24
Herbs . . . 25

24 Stamens 2. Leaves pinnate . . . OLEACEÆ (p. 168).
Stamens 4 or 5. Leaves ovate, toothed . CELASTRACEÆ (p. 56).
Stamens about 8. Leaves broadly lobed or angular. ACERACEÆ (p. 55).

25 Petals inserted on the tubular calyx near the top. LYTHRACEÆ (p. 89).
Petals inserted within the base of the calyx . . . 26

26 Leaves divided, cut, or toothed . . . GERANIACEÆ (p. 51).
Leaves quite entire . . . 27

27 Capsule 1-celled, with a central placenta and several seeds. CARYOPHYLLACEÆ (p. 32).
Capsule with a single seed . . . ILLECEBRACEÆ (p. 209).
Capsule and ovary divided into several cells . . . 28

28 Petals 3 or 4, with twice as many stamens. Flowers very minute . . . ELATINE (p. 44).
Petals 4 or 5. Stamens the same, or rarely one or two additional ones . . . 29

29 Calyx tubular, 5-toothed . . . FRANKENIA (p. 32).
Calyx many-toothed. Flowers very small . RADIOLA (p. 49).
Sepals 5, quite free . . . LINUM *catharticum* (p. 48).

30 Trees or shrubs . . . 31
Low procumbent heath-like under-shrub, with 3 petals and stamens . . . EMPETRUM (p. 225).
Herbs rarely slightly woody at the base . . . 34

31 Petals and stamens 6. Berry 1- or 2-seeded . BERBERIS (p. 9).
Petals 4 or 5. Stamens as many, or twice as many . . 32

32 Branches twiggy, with small green scale-like leaves. Capsule 1-celled. Seeds cottony . . . TAMARIX (p. 44).
Shrubs or trees, with flat leaves. Ovary and fruit (usually a berry) divided into cells . . . 33

33 Petals white, alternating with the stamens . . ILEX (p. 56).
Petals very small, green and behind the stamens, or none. RHAMNUS (p. 56).

34 Petals 4 . . . 35
Petals 5 . . . 36
Petals and stamens 6 . . . LYTHRUM (p. 89)

35 Leafless herbs, with brown scales. Stamens 8 MONOTROPA (p. 162).
Herbs with entire or divided leaves. Stamens 6, of which 2 are shorter, or rarely wanting . . . CRUCIFERÆ (p. 13).

36 Stamens 10 . . . 37
Stamens 5 . . . 38

37 {
  Style single, with a broad stigma. Leaves entire or minutely
toothed . . . . PYROLA (p. 161)
Two styles or 2 distinct stigmas. Leaves often toothed or
divided . . . . . . SAXIFRAGA (p. 94).
Five styles. Leaves of 3 leaflets . . . OXALIS (p. 54).
}

38 {
  Leaves all radical, or only one on the stem . . . 39
Stem-leaves several, entire 40
}

39 {
  Style filiform with 3 stigmas. Flowers minute with 2 sepals.
CLAYTONIA (p. 44).
Styles 3 to 5, each one deeply divided. Leaves fringed with
glandular hairs . . . . . . DROSERA (p. 98).
Stigmas 4, sessile. Leaves broad, entire, one on the stem.
PARNASSIA (p. 98).
Styles 5. Leaves all radical, entire . PLUMBAGINACEÆ (p. 206).
}

40 {
  Styles 3. Procumbent plant, with very small white and green
flowers . . . . . . CORRIGIOLA (p. 209).
Styles 5. Flowers blue . . . . . LINUM (p. 48).
}

Irregular Polypetals with one free, simple, or compound ovary.

41 {
  Flowers with a spur or pouch at the base . . . 42
Flowers not spurred 44
}

42 {
  Stamens numerous . . . . . DELPHINIUM (p. 8).
Stamens 6, united in two clusters . . FUMARIACEÆ (p. 12).
Stamens 5 43
}

43 {
  Sepals 5. Petals 5, spreading, one of them spurred VIOLA (p. 31).
Outer sepals. One inner sepal, large, hooded, and spurred.
Petals 1, outer, entire, 2 inner lobed . . IMPATIENS (p. 55).
Petals small, deeply cut. Stamens more than 8, free RESEDA (p. 29).
}

44 {
  Petals 5, papilionaceous. Stamens 10, all or 9 united.
PAPILIONACEÆ (p. 57).
Petals and sepals in pairs or in fours. Stamens 6 . 45
Sepals 5, of which 2 are large. Petals 3 or 5, small. Stamens
8, united in two clusters . . . POLYGALA (p. 32).
}

45 {
  Petals 4, spreading, 2 large and 2 small. Stamens free.
CRUCIFERÆ (p. 13).
Petals 4, small, erect in two pairs. Stamens united in two
clusters . . . . . . FUMARIACEÆ (p. 12).
}

Polypetals with an inferior ovary.

46 {
  Stamens 10 or fewer, of the same number as or twice the petals 47
Stamens indefinite, usually numerous . . ROSACEÆ (p. 75).
}

47 {
  Petals 5. Stamens 10 . . . . SAXIFRAGA (p. 94).
Petals 5. Stamens 5 48
Petals 3. Aquatic plants with diclinous flowers.
HYDROCHARIDACEÆ (p. 244).
Petals 2 or 4. Stamens 2, 4, or 8 . . . 49
}

48 {
  Herbs. Fruit separating into 2 dry 1-seeded carpels.
UMBELLIFERÆ (p. 100).
Shrubs. Fruit a berry, with several seeds . RIBES (p. 93).
Evergreen climber. Fruit a berry, with 2 to 5 seeds.
HEDERA (p. 115).
}

49 {
  Fruit a berry. Shrubs or herbs . . CORNUS (p. 115).
Fruit dry, capsular. Herbs . . . ONAGRACEÆ (p. 86).
}

Monopetals with an inferior ovary.

51 { Leaves alternate or radical 52
   { Leaves opposite or whorled 54

52 { Shrubs. Stamens 8 or 10. Fruit a berry . VACCINIUM (p. 157).
   { Climber. Flowers diœcious. Stamens 5, combined into 3.
   { Fruit a berry . . . . BRYONIA (p. 90).
   { Herbs with ternately divided leaves. Stamens 8 or 10. Fruit
   { a berry . . . . ADOXA (p. 116).
   { Herbs. Stamens 5. Fruit a capsule 53

53 { Stamens inserted within the base of the corolla.
   {   CAMPANULACEÆ (p. 153).
   { Stamens inserted in the tube of the corolla. Flowers small,
   { white . . . . SAMOLUS (p. 166).

54 { Leaves in whorls of four or more . . . RUBIACEÆ (p. 118).
   { Leaves opposite 55

55 { Stamens 1, 2, or 3 . . . . . VALERIANACEÆ (p. 121).
   { Stamens 4 or 5 56

56 { Flowers numerous, in heads, with a common involucre. Fruit
   { dry, 1-seeded. Stem herbaceous . DIPSACACEÆ (p. 123).
   { Flowers distinct or few together, without a common involucre.
   { Fruit often succulent. Stem usually shrubby or climbing.
   {   CAPRIFOLIACEÆ (p. 116).

Monopetals with a free ovary.

57 { Stamens twice as many as the lobes of the corolla . . . 58
   { Stamens equal in number to the lobes of the corolla or fewer . 61

58 { Flowers regular. Stamens distinct 60
   { Flowers very irregular. Stamens united 59

59 { Leaves much divided . . . . FUMARIACEÆ (p. 12).
   { Leaves with 3 leaflets . . . . TRIFOLIUM (p. 61).
   { Leaves entire . . . . . . POLYGALA (p. 32).

60 { Ovary single, of several cells. Leaves not peltate.
   {   ERICACEÆ (p. 157).
   { Ovaries several, distinct. Radical leaves peltate, fleshy.
   {   COTYLEDON (p. 90).

61 { Ovaries divided into two or four resembling naked seeds, in the
   { bottom of the calyx, with the style arising from between them 62
   { Ovary entire, of 1 or more cells, the style or stigma at the top . 63

62 { Leaves all opposite. Corolla 2-lipped, or seldom nearly regular.
   {   LABIATÆ (p. 194).
   { Leaves alternate (except sometimes the floral ones). Corolla
   { regular or rarely oblique . . . BORAGINACEÆ (p. 173).

63 { Corolla regular 64
   { Corolla irregular 80

64 { Stamens opposite the lobes of the corolla, and of the same
   { number . . . . . . PRIMULACEÆ (p. 162).
   { Stamens alternating with the lobes of the corolla, or fewer in
   { number 65

65 { Stamens 2. Leaves opposite 66
   { Stamens 3. Small herb, with minute white flowers MONTIA (p. 44).
   { Stamens 4 67
   { Stamens and divisions of the corolla 5 or more . . . 72

66 { Trees or shrubs . . . . . . OLEACEÆ (p. 168).
   { Herb. Corolla rotate . . . . VERONICA (p. 188).
   { No leaves. Stems thread-like, adhering to other plants.
   {   CUSCUTA (p. 172).

67 { Leaves alternate or radical 68
   { Leaves opposite 71

68 { Shrubs with evergreen leaves . . . . . ILEX (p. 56).
     Herbs 69

69 { Corolla scarious, deeply 4-lobed. Stamens longer than the
       corolla . . . . PLANTAGINACEÆ (p. 207).
     Corolla of the consistence of petals. Stamens shorter than
       the corolla 70

70 { Leaves narrow, entire . . . . . LIMOSELLA (p. 187).
     Leaves orbicular, crenate . . . . . SIBTHORPIA (p. 187).

71 { Leaves entire . . . . . . GENTIANACEÆ (p. 169).
     Leaves toothed or cut . . . . . VERBENA (p. 206).

72 { Fruit a berry 73
     Fruit a capsule 74

73 { Shrubs with evergreen leaves . . . . . ILEX (p. 56).
     Stem or branches herbaceous . . . . SOLANACEÆ (p. 178).

74 { Leaves opposite, entire 75
     Leaves alternate, or none 76

75 { Trailing plants with evergreen leaves. Two ovaries joining at
       the top into one style . . . . . VINCA (p. 168).
     Small procumbent shrubs, with very small evergreen leaves.
       Ovary single . . . . . LOISELEURIA (p. 159).
     Herbs. Ovary single . . . . GENTIANACEÆ (p. 169).

76 { Leaves divided 77
     Leaves undivided or none 78

77 { Leaves of 3 leaflets. Corolla hairy within. Aquatic plant.
                                            MENYANTHES (p. 171).
     Leaves pinnately cut. Corolla smooth. Erect herb.
                                            POLEMONIUM (p. 171).

78 { Aquatic plant, with floating orbicular leaves LIMNANTHEMUM (p. 171).
     Twining or procumbent plants. Corolla campanulate. Seeds
       2 or 4 in each capsule. . . . . CONVOLVULACEÆ (p. 172).
     Tall erect plants. Seeds numerous 79

79 { Corolla nearly rotate, the upper lobes overlapping the lower ones.
                                            VERBASCUM (p. 182).
     Corolla campanulate, or with a distinct tube, the lobes folded
       in the bud . . . . . . SOLANACEÆ (p. 178).

80 { Stamens 5, free 79
     Stamens 3. Small plant with minute white flowers MONTIA (p. 44).
     Stamens 2 or 4 81

81 { Corolla with a spur 82
     Corolla without a spur 83

82 { Two stamens. Capsule 1-celled . LENTIBULARIACEÆ (p. 166).
     Four stamens. Capsule 2-celled . SCROPHULARIACEÆ (p. 182).

83 { One or two seeds in the ovary or capsule VERBENACEÆ (p. 206).
     Several seeds in the capsule, or at least several ovules in the
       ovary 84

84 { Plant leafless, except scales of the colour of the stem. Capsule
       1-celled . . . . . . OROBANCHACEÆ (p. 180).
     Leaves green. Capsule 2-celled . SCROPHULARIACEÆ (p. 182).

Perianth simple or none.

85 { Floating or submerged plants 86
     Terrestrial herbs, or, if aquatic, erect from the bottom of the
       water, and projecting from it 93
     Trees or shrubs 141

1. *Floating Aquatic Plants.*

86 {
Small leaf-like fronds, attached two or three together, and floating without any stem   LEMNA (p. 237).
Leaves and flowers growing out of a distinct stem   .   .   . 87

87 {
Leaves deeply divided into capillary lobes   88
Leaves entire   89

88 {
Leaves pinnately divided.   Perianth 3-lobed MYRIOPHYLLUM (p. 99).
Leaves repeatedly forked.   Perianth none or many-lobed.
                                        CERATOPHYLLUM (p. 225).

89 {
Leaves opposite or whorled   90
Leaves in a radical submerged tuft   136
Leaves radical in floating tufts   .   .   HYDROCHARIS (p. 244).
Leaves alternate   92

90 {
Tube of the flower long and thread-like, resembling a pedicel.
                                ELODEA, HYDRILLA (p. 244).
Flowers sessile, or nearly so, in the axils of the leaves, or in stalked heads or spikes, without any stalk-like tube   . 91

91 {
One 4-lobed ovary.   Two styles   .   CALLITRICHE (p. 226).
Four ovaries, with distinct styles or stigmas NAIADACEÆ (p. 237).
One simple ovary and style   .   .   .   HIPPURIS (p. 99).

92 {
Flowers axillary.   Perianth none, or of 4 small scales.
                                        NAIADACEÆ (p. 237).
Flowers in globular heads, the upper head male, the lower female.
Perianth none, or of 1 to 6 small scales   SPARGANIUM (p. 235).
Flowers glumaceous.   Stamens 2 or 3   .   SCIRPUS *fluitans* (p. 274).
Perianth of 6 parts.   Stamens 6   JUNCUS *articulatus* (p. 266).
Perianth of 5 parts.   Stamens about 5 POLYGONUM *amphibium* (p. 219).

2. *Terrestrial Herbs, or, if Aquatic, erect.*

93 {
Flowers hermaphrodite, containing one or more ovaries and one or more stamens   94
Flowers diclinous, the stamens and ovaries either in separate perianths, or intermixed or variously arranged on the same spike, or within the same involucre, but separated by single scales only, without distinct perianths   .   .   . 125

94 {
Stamens more than 6   95
Stamens 6 or fewer   102

95 {
Stamens indefinite, usually numerous   .   .   . 96
Stamens about 12   97
Stamens 7 to 10   98

96 {
Stamens hypogynous.   Ovaries numerous   RANUNCULACEÆ (p. 1).
Stamens perigynous.   Ovaries few or single   ROSACEÆ (p. 75).

97 {
Perianth 3-lobed.   Capsule sessile   .   ASARUM (p. 221).
Perianth (involucre) with 5 small lobes or teeth.   Capsule stalked   .   .   .   .   .   . EUPHORBIA (p. 221).

98 {
Leaves radical, or in a single whorl on the stem   .   . 99
Leaves alternate or opposite   100

99 {
Leaves once or twice ternately divided.   Flowers in a small terminal head   .   .   .   .   . ADOXA (p. 116).
Leaves entire, rush-like, radical.   Flowers in a terminal umbel.
Plant aquatic   .   .   .   .   . BUTOMUS (p. 242).
Leaves entire, in a single whorl of four or five.   Flowers solitary, terminal   .   .   .   .   . PARIS (p. 257).

100 {
Leaves orbicular, crenate.   Capsule inferior, many-seeded.
                                CHRYSOSPLENIUM (p. 97).
Leaves entire.   Capsule several-seeded   CARYOPHYLLACEÆ (p. 32).
Leaves entire.   Capsule 1-seeded   101

101 { Leaves small, opposite. Capsule inferior   SCLERANTHUS (p. 209).
      Leaves alternate, with sheathing stipules   POLYGONUM (p. 217).

102 { Perianth coloured, and looking like a corolla   103
      Perianth herbaceous, and looking like a calyx or scales, or
          entirely wanting   111

103 { One or two anthers sessile on a central column or style. One
          of the six divisions of the perianth different from the others.
                                                    ORCHIDACEÆ (p. 245).
      Three to six stamens distinct from the style   .   .   .   104

104 { Leaves opposite or in whorls.   105
      Leaves alternate or radical   107

105 { Stamens 6. Capsule 2-celled, with several seeds   .   PEPLIS (p. 89).
      Stamens 5 or fewer. Ovary inferior   54
      Stamens 5. Ovary superior   106

106 { Capsule 1-seeded. Stipules small, scarious   ILLECEBRACEÆ (p. 209)
      Capsules several-seeded, 1-celled. No stipules   GLAUX (p. 165)

107 { Leaves pinnate, with stipules   .   .   SANGUISORBA (p. 82)
      Leaves pinnate or divided, without stipules.
                                                    UMBELLIFERÆ (p. 100).
      Leaves entire   108

108 { Stipules forming sheaths or rings round the stems. Nut superior,
          1-seeded .   .   .   .   .   .   POLYGONACEÆ (p. 215).
      No stipules   109

109 { Stamens and divisions of the flower 4 or 5   .   .   .   110
      Stamens and divisions of the flower 3 or 6. Leaves with
          parallel veins   154

110 { Styles 5. Ovary and capsule superior   .   PLUMBAGINACEÆ (p. 206).
      Styles 2. Ovary inferior   .   .   .   UMBELLIFERÆ (p. 100).
      Style 1. Ovary inferior   .   .   .   .   THESIUM (p. 221).

111 { Leaves opposite or whorled   112
      Leaves alternate or radical   117

      Fleshy, articulate, maritime plants, without leaves. Stamens
          1 or 2   .   .   .   .   .   .   SALICORNIA (p. 210).
112 { Leaves linear, whorled. Stamen 1 .   .   .   HIPPURIS (p. 99).
      Leaves opposite. Stamens 4, 5, or 6   113

113 { Ovary and capsule 1-seeded   114
      Ovary and capsule several-seeded   115

114 { Leaves small, with scarious stipules   .   ILLECEBRACEÆ (p. 209).
      No stipules   .   .   .   .   .   CHENOPODIACEÆ (p. 210).

115 { Ovary inferior. Stamens 4   .   .   .   LUDWIGIA (p. 88).
      Ovary superior   116

      Calyx 6-toothed. Stamens 6. Capsule 2-celled   .   PEPLIS (p. 89).
      Calyx 5-lobed. Stamens 5. Capsule 1-celled, several-seeded.
116 {   GLAUX (p. 165).
      Calyx of 4 or 5 sepals. Stamens 4 or 5. Capsule 1-celled,
          several-seeded .   .   .   .   CARYOPHYLLACEÆ (p. 32).

      Flowers glumaceous, consisting of chaffy scales alternating
          with each other, enclosing the stamens. Leaves linear.
          Stamens 2 or 3   165
117 { Perianth entire, oblique, projecting on one side into a lip. Sta-
          mens 6   .   .   .   .   .   ARISTOLOCHIACEÆ (p. 221).
      Perianth 4-, 5-, or 6-merous. Stamens 4, 5, or 6   .   118

118 { Two or more ovaries   .   .   .   .   .   ROSACEÆ (p. 75).
      A single ovary   119

119 { Perianth of 4 or 5 parts or teeth. Stamens usually 4 or 5   120
      Perianth of 6 divisions. Stamens 6   124

120 { Ovary inferior   .   .   .   .   .   .   THESIUM (p. 221).
      Ovary superior   121

121 { Seeds several in the capsule . . . . PLANTAGO (p. 207).
    { Seeds solitary 122

122 { Stipules leafy. Leaves broadly lobed or divided ROSACEÆ (p. 75).
    { Stipules membranous, sheathing the stem POLYGONACEÆ (p. 215).
    { Stipules minute or none 123

123 { Stamens 4 . . . . PARIETARIA (p. 227).
    { Stamens 5 . . . . CHENOPODIACEÆ (p. 210).

124 { Stem leafy. Stipules sheathing. Nut enclosed in three of the
    {   perianth-lobes . . . . RUMEX (p. 215).
    { Leaves linear, mostly radical. Capsule with 3 or more seeds . 161

125 { Stamens and pistils in distinct globular or cylindrical masses
    {   without separate perianths 166
    { Stamens about 12, with one pistil in a calyx-like involucre.
    {   EUPHORBIA (p. 221).
    { Flowers, male or female, each with a distinct perianth . . 126

126 { Stems long and climbing 127
    { Stems parasitic on trees with hard green forked branches.
    {   VISCUM (p. 115).
    { Stems terrestrial or aquatic, but neither climbing nor floating . 130

127 { Leaves opposite. Capsules in a head concealed by leafy bracts.
    {   HUMULUS (p. 227).
    { Leaves alternate. Berries red 128

128 { Leaves angular or lobed. Stem climbing by tendrils. Perianth
    {   5-lobed . . . . BRYONIA (p. 90).
    { Leaves entire, shining. Stem twining, without tendrils.
    {   Perianth 6-lobed . . . . . . TAMUS (p. 257).

129 { Male and female flowers on the same plant 131
    { Male and female flowers on different plants 139

130 { Flowers glumaceous, consisting of chaffy scales enclosing
    {   the stamens 165
    { Flowers of both sorts, or at least the males, with a distinct
    {   perianth of 3, 4, or more divisions 129

131 { Male perianth of 3 to 5 divisions 132
    { Male perianth of 6 divisions 138

132 { Stamens as many as the divisions of the perianth . . . 133
    { Stamens indefinite 137

133 { Male flowers in globular heads in a terminal raceme. Females
    {   axillary, joined two together in a large prickly burr, with
    {   incurved points . . . . . XANTHIUM (p. 130).
    { Flowers, male and female, distinct, or in heads, not prickly . 134

134 { Male perianth of 4 parts 135
    { Male perianth of 5 or 3 parts . . . CHENOPODIACEÆ (p. 210).

135 { Leaves all radical, linear and fleshy, or transparent. Marsh
    {   or water plants 136
    { Stems leafy. Leaves flat . . . . URTICACEÆ (p. 226).

136 { Male flowers one or two on a stalk, with very long stamens.
    {   Females sessile. . . . . . LITTORELLA (p. 209).
    { Male and female flowers minute, mixed together in a small
    {   terminal head . . . . . ERIOCAULON (p. 270).

137 { Leaves opposite, simple . . . MERCURIALIS (p. 224).
    { Leaves alternate, pinnate . . . . POTERIUM (p. 82).

138 { Leaves alternate, with sheathing stipules. Stamens 6. Nut
    {   enclosed in the calyx . . . . . RUMEX (p. 215).
    { Leaves small and fine, in tufts. Stamens 6. Fruit a berry.
    {   ASPARAGUS (p. 258).
    { Leaves small and heath-like. Stamens 3. Fruit a berry.
    {   EMPETRUM (p. 225).
    { Leaves radical, long, arrow-shaped. Stamens and carpels
    {   numerous. Aquatic plant . . . SAGITTARIA (p. 243).

139 { Flowers all male (a male specimen) **131**
    { Flowers all female (a female specimen) **140**
       Perianth 6-cleft, the 3 inner segments larger. Styles 3, with
         short fringed stigmas. Leaves alternate or radical.
                                       RUMEX (p. 215).

140 { Perianth 2- or 4-cleft. Stigma single, sessile, tufted. Leaves
    { opposite, stinging . . . . . . URTICA (p. 226).
       Perianth 3-cleft. Styles 2, simple. Leaves opposite, not sting-
       ing . . . . . . MERCURIALIS (p. 224).

3. *Trees or Shrubs.*

141 { Leaves opposite **142**
    { Leaves alternate or in tufts **145**

142 { Leaves divided, lobed or angular, deciduous . . . **143**
    { Leaves entire, evergreen **144**

143 { Leaves lobed or angular. Stamens about 8. Fruit with two
    { diverging wings . . . . . . ACER (p. 55).
    { Leaves pinnate. Stamens in pairs, collected in clusters. Fruit
    { with one erect wing . . . . . FRAXINUS (p. 168).

144 { Parasitic shrub with green dichotomous stems. Fruit a berry.
    { . . . . VISCUM (p. 115).
    { Erect branching shrub with shining leaves. Fruit a few-
    { seeded capsule . . . . . . BUXUS (p. 225).

145 { Male flowers in catkins, separated by scales only. Females
    { solitary or in clusters, or in catkins, usually different from
    { the males **146**
    { Flowers hermaphrodite or diclinous, each with a distinct
    { perianth **147**

146 { Leaves entire and mostly evergreen, needle-like, or narrow or
    { scale-like. Anthers sessile on the catkin-scales.
    { . . . . CONIFERÆ (p. 234).
    { Leaves flat, mostly toothed. Stamens distinct from the scales.
    { . . . . AMENTACEÆ (p. 228).

147 { Flowers diœcious. Male perianth of 2 or 6 scales . . . **148**
    { Flowers hermaphrodite or polygamous. Perianth regular, of
    { 3 to 5 divisions **149**

148 { Erect shrub. Male perianth of 2 scales . HIPPOPHÆ (p. 221).
    { Procumbent undershrub. Perianth of 6 scales EMPETRUM (p. 225).

149 { Trees. Stamens opposite the lobes of the perianth. Fruit
    { thin, like a small leaf . . . ULMUS (p. 227).
    { Evergreen climber. Fruit a berry . . HEDERA (p. 115).
    { Shrubs. Fruit a berry **150**

150 { Flowers on the under side of the ' leaves ' (cladodes) RUSCUS (p. 259).
    { Flowers on the stem or branches **151**

151 { Flowers very small, green and open. Stamens 4 or 5, alternat-
    { ing with the lobes of the perianth . . RHAMNUS (p. 56).
    { Flowers with a conspicuous tube, often coloured. Stamens 8.
    { . . . . DAPHNE (p. 220).

Monocotyledons.

152 { Perianth, or at least the inner segments, coloured and looking
    { like a corolla, or, if green, soft and yellowish . . **153**
    { Perianth green or brown, or reduced to mere scales, or none
    { at all **159**

153 { One or two anthers sessile on a central column or style. One
    { of the six divisions of the perianth different from the others.
    { . . . . ORCHIDACEÆ (p. 245).
    { Three or more distinct stamens **154**

154 { Ovaries several, quite distinct, or, if cohering, each with a distinct style or stigma*   .   .   .   .   ALISMACEÆ (p. 242).
{ Ovary single, 3-celled   155

155 { Ovary inferior   156
{ Ovary superior   .   .   .   .   .   .   LILIACEÆ (p. 257).

156 { Floating or submerged plants   .   HYDROCHARIDACEÆ (p. 244).
{ Terrestrial or marsh plants   157

157 { Stamens 3 .   .   .   .   .   .   IRIDACEÆ (p. 254).
{ Stamens 6   158

158 { Climbing plant with alternate net-veined leaves   TAMUS (p. 257).
{ Bulbous herbs   .   .   .   .   .   AMARYLLIDACEÆ (p. 256).

159 { Floating or submerged plants   86
{ Terrestrial plants, or, if aquatic, erect from the bottom of the water and projecting above it   160

160 { Leaves in a single whorl of 4 or 5, with netted veins. Perianth-segments, and stamens, 8 or 10 .   .   .   PARIS (p. 257).
{ Leaves radical or alternate, linear or cylindrical, with parallel veins (veins netted in Arum)   161

161 { Perianth of 6 or 4 segments. Stamens as many or half as many   162
{ Flowers glumaceous, consisting of alternate chaffy scales, enclosing the stamens and pistil in the same or separate scales   165
{ Stamens and pistils in dense heads or spikes, without distinct perianths   166

162 { One style, with 2 or 3 linear stigmas   163
{ One ovary, with 3 distinct styles or stigmas   .   .   .   164
{ Three distinct ovaries   .   .   .   .   SCHEUCHZERIA (p. 242).

163 { Flowers minute, unisexual, in a globular head ERIOCAULON (p. 270).
{ Flowers complete, distinct, or clustered, or panicled JUNCACEÆ (p. 265).

164 { Three short styles   .   .   .   .   .   TOFIELDIA (p. 264).
{ Three sessile stigmas   .   .   .   .   .   TRIGLOCHIN (p. 242).

165 { Flowers with a single scale under each set of stamens and pistil. Sheath of the leaves closed round the stem CYPERACEÆ (p. 270).
{ Flowers enclosed in 2 or more scales. Sheath of the leaves usually split open on the side opposite the blade GRAMINEÆ (p. 289).

166 { Fruit a berry. Leaves usually broad   .   .   ARACEÆ (p. 236).
{ Fruit a dry nut. Leaves linear and sedge-like TYPHACEÆ (p. 235).

II. CRYPTOGAMS. (*No Stamens or Pistil.*)

1 { Plants with distinct roots and stems or rootstocks, with leaves or green branches   2
{ Plants variously shaped, without distinct roots, stems, and leaves, seldom green unless aquatic   .   CELLULAR CRYPTOGAMS.

2 { Fructification in terminal spikes   3
{ Fructification radical or in the axils of small leaves   .   .   4
{ Fructification on the back of the leaves or leaf-like branches. FILICES (p. 319).
{ Fructification on the submerged segments of minute floating leaves. Aquatic plant   .   .   .   AZOLLA (p. 317).
{ Fructification on the whorled leaves. Aquatic plant   .   CHARAS.

3 { Stems leafless, jointed, simple, or with whorled branches. EQUISETUM (p. 317).
{ Stems bearing numerous small leaves. Spores of one kind. LYCOPODIUM (p. 314).
{ Stems bearing numerous small leaves. Spores of two kinds. SELAGINELLA (p. 316).
{ Stem bearing a simple or branched leaf below the spike. FILICES (p. 319).

* See also SCHEUCHZERIA and TRIGLOCHIN, p. 242.

4 { Spore-cases sessile 5
   { Spore-cases stalked 6

5 { Spore-cases small, in the axils of small leaves or bracts.
   {   LYCOPODIUM (p. 314).
   { Spore-cases in the enlarged base of linear submerged leaves.
   {   ISOETES (p. 316).
   { Spore-cases (or involucres) globular on the rootstock at the
   {   base of linear leaf-like fronds . . . PILULARIA (p. 316).

6 { Spore-cases globular or urn-shaped, opening with a lid   MOSSES.
   { Spore-cases opening in valves . . . . HEPATICÆ.

ILLUSTRATIONS

OF THE

BRITISH FLORA

——

Class I.   DICOTYLEDONS.

Sub-class 1.   THALAMIFLORÆ.

I. RANUNCULACEÆ.

1. Clematis Vitalba L.

Traveller's Joy, Old Man's Beard.

2. Thalictrum alpinum L.

Alpine Meadow-Rue.

3. Thalictrum minus **L.**

Lesser Meadow-Rue.

4. Thalictrum flavum L.

Common Meadow Rue; Y.

5. Anemone Pulsatilla L.

Pasque-flower; P.

6. Anemone nemorosa L.

Wood Anemone.

7. **Adonis annua L.**
A. autumnalis L.
Pheasant's Eye ; R.

8. **Myosurus minimus L.**
Mousetail ; Y.

9. **Ranunculus aquatilis L.**
Water Crowfoot.

10. **Ranunculus hederaceus L.**
Ivy-leaved Crowfoot.

11. Ranunculus Lingua L.
Great Spearwort ; Y.

12. Ranunculus Flammula L.
Lesser Spearwort ; Y.

13. Ranunculus ophioglossifolius
Vill.
Snaketongue Crowfoot ; Y.

14. Ranunculus Ficaria L.
Pilewort, Lesser Celandine ; Y.

15. Ranunculus sceleratus L.

Celery-leaved Crowfoot; Y.

16. Ranunculus auricomus L.

Goldilocks; Y.

17. Ranunculus acris L.

Crowfoot, Buttercup; Y.

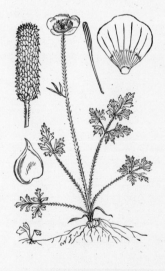

18. Ranunculus repens L.

Creeping Buttercup; Y.

19. Ranunculus flabellatus Desf.

Fine-leaved Buttercup; Y.

20. Ranunculus bulbosus L.
Bulbous Buttercup; Y.

21. Ranunculus sardous Crantz.
R. hirsutus Curt.
Hairy Buttercup; Y.

22. Ranunculus parviflorus L.
Small-flowered Buttercup; Y.

23 Ranunculus arvensis L.
Corn Buttercup; Y.

24. Caltha palustris L.

Marsh Marigold ; Y.

25. Trollius europæus L.

Globeflower ; Y.

26. Helleborus viridis L.

Green Hellebore, Bear's-foot ; G.

27. Helleborus fœtidus L.

Stinking H., Steer wort ; Y.

28. Aquilegia vulgaris L.

Columbine; B.

29. Delphinium Ajacis L.

Larkspur; B., R., W.

30. Aconitum Napellus L.

Monkshood, Wolfsbane; B

31. Actæa spicata L.

Baneberry, Herb Christopher.

32 Pæonia officinalis L.

Peony; R.

33. Berberis vulgaris L.

Barberry; Y.

III. NYMPHÆACEÆ

34. Nymphæa alba L.

White Waterlily.

35. Nuphar luteum Sm.

Yellow Waterlily.

36. Papaver somniferum L.
Opium Poppy.

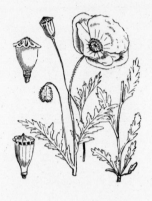

37. Papaver Rhœas L.
Field Poppy ; R.

38. Papaver dubium L.
Long-headed Poppy ; R.

39. Papaver hybridum L.
Rough Poppy ; R.

40 Papaver Argemone L.

Pale Poppy ; R.

41. Meconopsis cambrica Vig.

Welsh Poppy ; Y.

42. Chelidonium majus L.

Celandine ; Y.

43. Rœmeria hybrida DC.

Roemeria ; P.

44. Glaucium flavum Crantz.

G. luteum Scop.

Horned Poppy ; Y.

45. Fumaria officinalis L.

Fumitory; W.,'R.

46. Corydalis lutea DC.

Yellow Corydalis.

47. Corydalis claviculata DC.

Climbing Corydalis.

48. Matthiola incana Br.

Stock, Gilliflower; P.

49. Matthiola sinuata Br.

Sea Stock; P.

50. Cheiranthus Cheiri L.

Wallflower; Y.-R.

51. Barbarea vulgaris Br.

Wintercress, Yellow Rocket.

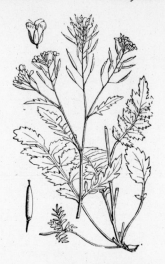

52. Nasturtium officinale Br.

Common Watercress.

53. Nasturtium sylvestre Br.

Creeping Watercress; Y.

54. Nasturtium palustre DC.

Marsh Watercress; Y.

55. Nasturtium amphibium Br.

Great Watercress; Y.

56. Arabis glabra Bernh.

A. perfoliata Lam.

Glabrous Rockcress, Tower Mustard.

57. Arabis Turrita L.

Tower Rockcress, Towercress ; Y.-W.

58. Arabis hirsuta Scop.

Hairy Rockcress.

59. Arabis alpina L.

Alpine Rockcress.

60. **Arabis ciliata Br.**
Fringed Rockcress.

61. **Arabis Thaliana L.**
Thalecress, Wallcress.

63. **Arabis petræa Lam.**
Northern Rockcress.

62. **Arabis stricta Huds.**
Bristol Rockcress.

64. **Cardamine amara L.**
Large Bittercress

65. Cardamine pratensis L.

Meadow Bittercress, Ladies' Smock.
Cuckoo-flower ; W.-Pk.

66. Cardamine impatiens.

Narrow-leaved Bittercress.

67. Cardamine hirsuta L.

Hairy Bittercress.

68. Cardamine bulbifera Crantz.

Coralroot.

69. Hesperis matronalis L.

Dame's Violet; P.

70. Sisymbrium officinale Scop.

Hedge Mustard; Y.

71. Sisymbrium Irio L.

London Rocket; Y.

72. Sisymbrium Sophia L.

Flixweed; Y.

73. Alliaria officinalis Andrz.

Garlic-Mustard, Sauce-alone, Jack-by-the-hedge.

74. Erysimum cheiranthoides L.

Treacle Mustard; Y.

75. Erysimum orientale Br.

Hare's-ear; Y.-W.

76. Brassica tenuifolia Boiss.

Wall Mustard, Rocket; Y.

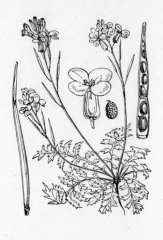

77. Brassica muralis Boiss.

Stinkweed; Y.

78. Brassica monensis Huds.

Isle of Man Cabbage; Y.

79. Brassica oleracea L.

Wild Cabbage; Y.

80. Brassica campestris L.

Field Cabbage; Y.

81. Brassica alba Boiss.

Cultivated Mustard; Y.

82. Brassica Sinapis Visiani.

Charlock, Wild Mustard; Y.

83. Brassica nigra Koch.

Black Mustard; Y.

84. Brassica adpressa Boiss.

Hoary B.; Y.

D

85. Cochlearia Armoracia L.

Horseradish.

86. Cochlearia officinalis L.

Scurvy-grass.

87. Alyssum alyssoides L.

A. calycinum L.

Small Alison; Y.

88. Alyssum maritimum L.

Sweet Alison.

89. Draba aizoides L.
Yellow Whitlow Grass.

91. Draba incana L.
Hoary Whitlow Grass.

90. Draba rupestris Br.
D. hirta Sm.
Rock Whitlow Grass.

93. Draba verna L.
Common Whitlow Grass.

92. Draba muralis L.
Wall Whitlow Grass.

94. Camelina sativa Crantz.
Gold of Pleasure; Y·

95. Subularia aquatica L.
Awlwort.

96. Thlaspi arvense L.
Mithridate Mustard, Pennycress.

97. Thlaspi perfoliatum L.
Perfoliate Pennycress.

98. Thlaspi alpestre L.
Alpine Pennycress.

99. Teesdalia nudicaulis Br.
Teesdalia

100. Iberis amara L.
Bitter Candytuft.

101. Hutchinsia petræa Br.
Rock H.

102. Capsella Bursa-pastoris Medik.

Shepherd's-purse.

103. Lepidium campestre Br.

Pepperwort.

104. Lepidium Smithii Hook.

Smith's Cress.

105. Lepidium Draba L.

Hoary Cress.

106. Lepidium latifolium L.
Dittander.

107. Lepidium ruderale L.
Narrow-leaved Cress.

108. Coronopus Ruellii All.
Senebiera Coronopus Poir.
Swine-cress, Wartcress.

109. Coronopus didymus Sm.
Senebiera didyma Sm.
Lesser Swine-cress.

110. Isatis tinctoria L.
Woad; Y.

111. Cakile maritima Scop.
Sea Rocket.

112. Crambe maritima L.
Seakale.

113. Raphanus Raphanistrum L.
Wild Radish, Jointed or White Charlock

114. Reseda luteola L.
Weld, Yellow Weed, Dyer's Rocket; Y.

115. Reseda lutea L.
Cut-leaved Mignonette; Y.

116. Reseda alba L.
White Mignonette.

117. Helianthemum guttatum Mill.

Spotted Rockrose; Y.

118. Helianthemum canum Baum.

Hoary Rockrose; Y.

119. Helianthemum Chamæcistus Mill.

H. vulgare Gærtn.

Common Rockrose; Y.

120 Helianthemum polifolium Mill.

White Rockrose.

121. Viola palustris L.

Marsh Violet.

122. Viola odorata L.

Sweet Violet.

124. Viola rupestris Schm.

V. arenaria DC.

Sand Violet.

125. Viola canina L.

Dog Violet.

123. Viola hirta L.

Hairy Violet.

126. Viola tricolor L.
Heartsease, Pansy; P., W., Y.

127. Polygala vulgaris L.
Milkwort; B., Pk., W.

XI. FRANKENIACEÆ

XII. CARYOPHYLLACEÆ

128. Frankenia lævis L.
Sea-heath; Pk.

129. Dianthus prolifer L.
Proliferons Pink.

130. Dianthus Armeria L.
Deptford Pink.

131. Dianthus deltoides L.
Maiden Pink.

132. Dianthus cæsius L.
Cheddar Pink.

133. Saponaria officinalis L.
Soapwort; Ph.-W.

134. Silene acaulis L.
Dwarf Catchfly, Moss Campion   P.

135. Silene Cucubalus Wibel.
Bladder Campion, White-Bottle.

136. Silene Otites Wibel.
Spanish Catchfly; Y.-G.

137. Silene nutans L.
Nottingham Catchfly.

138. Silene gallica L.
Small-flowered Catchfly.

139. Silene conica L.
Striated Catchfly; Pk.

140. Silene noctiflora L.
Night-flowering Catchfly.

141. Lychnis alba Mill.
L. vespertina Sibth.
White Campion.

142. Lychnis dioica L.
L. diurna Sibth.

Red Campion.

143. Lychnis Githago Scop.

Corn Cockle; R.

144. Lychnis Flos-cuculi L.
Ragged Robin; R.

145. Lychnis Viscaria L.
Viscid Campion; R.

146. Lychnis alpina L.
Alpine Campion; Pk.

147. Sagina procumbens L.
Procumbent Pearlwort.

148. Sagina saginoides Dalla T.
S. Linnæi Presl.
Alpine Pearlwort.

149. Sagina nodosa Fenzl.
Knotted Pearlwort.

150. Arenaria sedoides Kit.
A. Cherleri Benth.
Cyphel.

151. Arenaria verna L.
Vernal Sandwort.

152. Arenaria uliginosa Schl.
Bog Sandwort.

153. Arenaria tenuifolia L.
Fine-leaved Sandwort.

154. Arenaria peploides L.
Sea Purslane.

155. Arenaria serpyllifolia **L.**
Thyme-leaved Sandwort.

156. Arenaria ciliata L.
Fringed Sandwort.

157. Arenaria trinervia L.
Three-nerved Sandwort

158. Mœnchia erecta Gaertn.
Upright Mænchia.

159. Holosteum umbellatum L.
Holosteum.

160. Cerastium vulgatum L.
Mouse-ear Chickweed.

161. Cerastium arvense L.
Field Mouse-ear Chickweed.

162. Cerastium alpinum L.
Alpine Mouse-ear Chickweed.

163. Cerastium cerastoides Britton.
C. trigynum Vill.
Starwort Mouse-ear Chickweed.

164. Stellaria aquatica Scop.
Water Stitchwort.

165. Stellaria nemorum L.
Wood Stitchwort.

166. Stellaria media Vill.
Chickweed.

167. Stellaria uliginosa Murr.
Bog Stitchwort.

168. Stellaria graminea L.
Lesser Stitchwort.

169. Stellaria Dilleniana Moench.
S. palustris Retz.
Marsh Stitchwort.

170. Stellaria Holostea L.
Greater Stitchwort.

171. Spergularia rubra
J. & C. Presl.
Sandspurrey; Pk.

172. Spergula arvensis L.
Corn Spurrey.

173. Polycarpon tetraphyllum L.
Four-leaved Polycarpon.

174. Claytonia perfoliata Donn.
Perfoliate Claytonia.

175. Montia fontana L.
Blinks, Water Chickweed.

XIV. TAMARICACEÆ

176. Tamarix gallica L.
Tamarisk; Pk.

XV. ELATINACEÆ

177. Elatine hexandra DC.
Six-stamened Waterwort; R.

178. Elatine Hydropiper L.
Eight-stamened Waterwort; R.

179. Hypericum calycinum L.
Aaron's Beard, Rose of Sharon; Y.

180. Hypericum Androsæmum L.
Tutsan; Y.

181. Hypericum perforatum L.
Common St. John's-wort; Y

182. Hypericum maculatum Crantz.
H. dubium Leers.
Imperforate St. John's-wort; Y.

183. Hypericum quadrangulum L
Square-stalked St. John's-wort; Y.

184. Hypericum humifusum L.
Trailing St. John's-wort; Y.

185. Hypericum linarifolium Vahl.
Flax-leaved St. John's-wort; Y

186. Hypericum pulchrum L.

Slender St. John's-wort; Y.

187. Hypericum hirsutum L.

Hairy St. John's-wort; Y.

188. Hypericum montanum L.

Mountain St. John's-wort; Y.

189. Hypericum elodes L.

Marsh St. John's-wort; Y

190. Linum usitatissimum L.
Common Flax, Linseed; *B.*

191. Linum perenne L.
Perennial Flax; *B.*

192. Linum bienne Mill.
L. angustifolium Huds.
Pale Flax; *B.*

193. Linum catharticum L.
Cathartic Flax.

194. Radiola linoides Roth.

    ‹ R. Millegrana Sm.

                 Allseed.

195. Lavatera arborea L.

        Tree Mallow ; R.

196. Malva rotundifolia L.

    Dwarf Mallow ; B.

197. Malva sylvestris L.

    Common Mallow ; P.

198. Malva moschata L.

Musk Mallow; R.

199. Althæa officinalis L.

Marsh Mallow; R.

XIX. TILIACEÆ

200. Althæa hirsuta L.

Hispid A.; B.

201. Tilia europæa L.

Lime-tree; G.

202. Geranium sanguineum L.
Blood-red Crane's-Bill.

203. Geranium phæum L.
Dusky Crane's-Bill ; P.

204. Geranium sylvaticum L.
Wood Crane's-Bill ; P.

205. Geranium pratense L.
Meadow Crane's-Bill ; B

206. Geranium pyrenaicum Burm. f.
Mountain Crane's-Bill; P.

207. Geranium Robertianum L.
Herb-Robert; R.-P.

208. Geranium lucidum L.
Shining Crane's-Bill; R.

209. Geranium molle L.
Dove's-foot Crane's Bill; P.

210. Geranium pusillum L.
Small-flowered Crane's-Bill; P.

211. Geranium rotundifolium L.
Round-leaved Crane's-Bill; P.

212. Geranium dissectum L
Cut-leaved Crane's-Bill; P.

213. Geranium columbinum L.
Long-stalked Crane's-Bill; P.

214. Erodium cicutarium L'Hér.
Common Stork's-Bill ; P., Pk.

215. Erodium moschatum L'Hér.
Musk Stork's-Bill ; B.-P.

216. Erodium maritimum L'Hér.
Sea Stork's-Bill ; R.-P.

217. Oxalis Acetosella L.
Wood-sorrel.

218. Oxalis corniculata L.
Procumbent O.; Y.

219. Impatiens Noli-tangere L.
Yellow Balsam, Touch-me-not.

220. Impatiens biflora Walt.
I. fulva Nutt.
Orange Balsam.

XXI. ACERACEÆ

221. Acer campestre L.
Maple ; G.

222. Acer Pseudo-platanus L.

Sycamore ; G.

223. Ilex Aquifolium L.

Holly.

XXIII. CELASTRACEÆ

224. Euonymus europæus L.

Spindle-tree ; G.

XXIV. RHAMNACEÆ

225. Rhamnus catharticus L.

Buckthorn ; G.

226. Rhamnus Frangula L.

Alder Buckthorn; G.

227. Ulex europæus L.

Furze, Gorse, Whin; Y.

228. Ulex minor Roth.

U. nanus Forst.

Dwarf Furze; Y.

229. Genista tinctoria L.

Dyer's Greenweed; Y.

230. Genista pilosa L.
Hairy Greenweed; Y.

231. Genista anglica L.
Needle Furze; Y.

232. Cytisus scoparius Link.
Common Broom; Y.

233. Ononis arvensis L.
Restharrow; Pk.

234. Ononis reclinata L.
Small Restharrow; Pk.

235. Medicago falcata L.
Sickle Medick; Y.

236. Medicago sativa L.
Lucerne; P., B.

237. Medicago lupulina L.
Black Medick, Nonsuch; Y.

238. Medicago hispida Gaertn.
M. denticulata Willd.
Toothed Medick ; Y.

239. Medicago arabica All.
M. maculata Sibth.
Spotted Medick ; Y.

240. Medicago minima Bart.
Bur Medick ; Y.

241. Melilotus officinalis Willd.
Melilot ; Y.

242. Melilotus arvensis Wallr.
Field Melilot ; **Y.**

243. Melilotus alba Desr.
White Melilot.

244. Trigonella purpurascens Lam.
Fenugreek ; *Y.*

245. Trifolium incarnatum L.
Crimson Clover.

246. Trifolium arvense L.
Hare's-foot Clover.

247. Trifolium stellatum L.
Starry Clover.

248. Trifolium ochroleucum Huds.
Sulphur Clover.

249. Trifolium pratense L.
Red or Purple Clover.

250. Trifolium medium L.

Zigzag or Meadow Clover; P.

251. Trifolium squamosum L.

T. maritimum Huds.

Sea Clover; Pk.

252. Trifolium striatum L.

Knotted Clover; R.

253. Trifolium Bocconi Savi.

Boccone's Clover; R.

254. Trifolium scabrum L.
Rough Clover.

255. Trifolium strictum L.
Upright Clover; R

256. Trifolium glomeratum L.
Clustered Clover; Pk.

257. Trifolium suffocatum L.
Suffocated Clover.

258. Trifolium resupinatum L.
Reversed Clover ; Pk.

259. Trifolium subterraneum L.
Subterranean Clover.

260. Trifolium fragiferum L.
Strawberry Clover ; Pk.

261. Trifolium repens L.
White or Dutch Clover.

262. Trifolium hybridum L.
Alsike Clover ; P.

263 Trifolium campestre Schreb.
T. procumbens L.
Hop Trefoil ; Y.

264. Trifolium dubium Sibth.
T· minus Sm.
Lesser Clover ; Y.

265. Trifolium filiforme L.
Slender Clover ; Y.

266. Lotus corniculatus L.

Bird's-foot Trefoil; Y.

267. Lotus angustissimus L.

Slender L.; Y.

268. Anthyllis Vulneraria L.

Kidney Vetch, Lady's-fingers; Y.-R.

269. Astragalus danicus Retz.

Purple Milk-Vetch.

270. Astragalus alpinus L.

Alpine Milkvetch; P.

271. Astragalus glycyphyllos L.

Milkvetch; Y.

272. Oxytropis campestris DC.

Yellow O.

272. Oxytropis uralensis DC.

Purple O.

274. Ornithopus pinnatus Druce.

O. ebracteatus Brot.

Sand Bird's-foot ; Y.

275. Ornithopus perpusillus L.

Common Bird's-foot ; Y.

276. Hippocrepis comosa L.

Horseshoe Vetch ; Y.

277. Onobrychis viciæfolia Scop.

O. sativa Lam.

Sainfoin ; Pk.

278. Vicia hirsuta S.F.Gray.
Hairy Vetch, Tare; B.

279. Vicia tetrasperma Mœnch.
Slender Vetch; B.

280. Vicia Cracca L.
Tufted Vetch; P.

281. Vicia sylvatica L.
Wood Vetch.

282. Vicia Orobus DC.

Upright Vetch; P.-W.

283. Vicia sepium L.

Bush Vetch; P.

284. Vicia lutea L.

Yellow Vetch.

285. Vicia sativa L.

Common Vetch; P.

286. Vicia lathyroides L.

Spring Vetch; P.

287. Vicia bithynica L.

Bithynian Vetch; F.

288. Lathyrus Nissolia L.

Grass Vetchling; R.

289. Lathyrus Aphaca L.

Yellow Vetchling.

290. Lathyrus hirsutus L.
Rough Pea ; R.

291. Lathyrus pratensis L.
Meadow Pea ; Y.

292. Lathyrus tuberosus L.
Earth-nut Pea ; P.

293. Lathyrus sylvestris L.
Everlasting Pea ; R.-P.

294. Lathyrus palustris L.
Marsh Pea; B.-P.

295. Lathyrus maritimus Bigel.
Sea Pea; B.-P.

296. Lathyrus montanus Bernh.
L. macrorrhizus Wimm.
Tuberous Pea; R.-P.

297. Lathyrus niger Bernh.
Black Pea; P.

298. Prunus spinosa L.

Blackthorn, Sloe.

299. Prunus Cerasus L.

Wild Cherry.

300. Prunus Padus L.

Birdcherry.

301. Spiræa salicifolia L.

Willow S.; Pk.

302. Spiræa Ulmaria L.

Meadow-sweet.

303. Spiræa Filipendula L.

Dropwort.

304. Dryas octopetala L.

White D.

305. Geum urbanum L.

Avens, Herb-Bennet; Y.

306. Geum rivale L.

Water Avens ; P.

307 Rubus Idæus L.

Raspberry.

308. Rubus fruticosus L.

Bramble, Blackberry.

309. Rubus cæsius L.

Dewberry.

310. Rubus saxatilis L.
Stone Bramble.

311. Rubus Chamæmorus L.
Cloudberry.

312. Fragaria vesca L.
Strawberry.

313. Potentilla sterilis Garcke.
P. Fragariastrum Ehrh.
Strawberry-leaved P.

314. Potentilla reptans L.
Cinquefoil; Y.

315. Potentilla erecta Hampe.
P. Tormentilla Neck.
Tormentil; Y.

316. Potentilla argentea L.
Hoary P.; Y

317. Potentilla verna L.
Spring P.; Y.

318   Potentilla Sibbaldi Hall. f.

Sibbaldia ;   Y.

319.   Potentilla fruticosa L.

Shrubby P. ;   Y.

320.   Potentilla Anserina L.

Silver-weed;   Y.

321.   Potentilla rupestris L.

Rock P.

322. Potentilla palustris Scop.
Marsh Cinquefoil; P.

323. Alchemilla vulgaris L.
Lady's-mantle; G.

24. Alchemilla alpina L.
Alpine Lady's-mantle; G.

325. Alchemilla arvensis Scop.
Parsley Piert; G.

326. Sanguisorba officinalis L.
Great Burnet; P.

327. Poterium Sanguisorba L.
Salad Burnet; G.

328. Agrimonia Eupatoria L.
Agrimony; Y.

329. Rosa spinosissima L.
R. pimpinellifolia L.
Burnet, Scotch Rose.

330. Rosa villosa L.
Downy Rose.

331. Rosa eglanteria L.
R. rubiginosa L.
Sweetbriar; Pk.

332. Rosa canina L.
Dog Rose; Pk., W.

333. Rosa arvensis Huds.
Field Rose.

334. Pyrus communis L.

Pear.

335. Pyrus Malus L.

Crab-apple ; W., Pk.

336. Pyrus Aria Ehrh.

White Beam.

337. Pyrus torminalis Ehrh.

Wild Service-tree.

338. Pyrus Aucuparia Gærtn.
Rowan-tree, Mountain Ash.

339. Cratægus Oxyacantha L.
Hawthorn, May, Whitethorn.

340. Cotoneaster integerrimus Medik.
C. vulgaris Lindl.
Cotoneaster.

341. Mespilus germanica L.
Medlar.

342. Epilobium angustifolium L.

French Willow, Rose-bay; R.

343. Epilobium hirsutum L.

Great Willow-herb, Codlins-and-Cream; R.

344. Epilobium parviflorum Schreb.

Hoary Willow-herb; R.

345. Epilobium montanum L.

Broad-leaved Willow-herb; Pk.

346. Epilobium roseum Schreb.
Pale Willow-herb; Pk.

347. Epilobium tetragonum L.
Square-stemmed Willow-herb; Pk.

348. Epilobium palustre L.
Marsh Willow-herb; Pk.

349. Epilobium alsinefolium Vill.
Chickweed Willow-herb; Pk.

350. Epilobium alpinum L.
Alpine Willow-herb ; Pk.

351. Œnothera Lamarckiana Ser.
O. biennis L.
Evening Primrose ; Y.

352. Ludwigia palustris Ell.
Marsh L.

353. Circæa lutetiana L.
Enchanter's Nightshade.

354. Circæa alpina L.

Alpine Enchanter's Nightshade.

355. Lythrum Salicaria L.

Purple Loosestrife.

356. Lythrum hyssopifolium L.

Hyssop Loosestrife; P.

357. Peplis Portula L.

Water Purslane.

358. Bryonia dioica Jacq.
Bryony; Y.

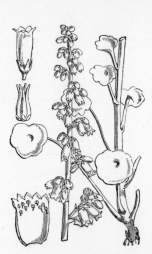

360. Cotyledon Umbilicus L.
Pennywort, Navelwort; G.

359. Tillæa muscosa L.
Mossy T.

359*a.* Tillæa aquatica L.
Water T.

361. Sedum roseum Scop.
S. Rhodiola DC.
Roseroot, Midsummer-men; Y.(P.)

362. Sedum Telephium L.

Orpine, Livelong ; P.

363. Sedum anglicum Huds

English Stonecrop.

364. Sedum dasyphyllum L.

Thick-leaved Stonecrop.

365. Sedum album L.

White Stonecrop.

366. Sedum villosum L.
Hairy Stonecrop; R.

367. Sedum acre L.
Wall-pepper; Y.

368. Sedum sexangulare L.
Tasteless Stonecrop; Y.

369. Sedum rupestre L.
Rock Stonecrop; Y.

370. Sedum reflexum L.
Reflexed-leaved Stonecrop; Y.

371. Sempervivum tectorum L.
Houseleek; Pk.

XXXI. RIBESIACEÆ

372. Ribes Grossularia L.
Gooseberry: G.

373. Ribes rubrum L.
Red and White Currant; G. W.

374. Ribes alpinum L.
Mountain Currant.

375. Ribes nigrum L.
Black Currant.

XXXII. SAXIFRAGACEÆ

376. Saxifraga oppositifolia L.
Purple Saxifrage.

377. Saxifraga aizoides L.
Yellow Saxifrage.

378. Saxifraga Hirculus L.
Marsh Saxifrage; Y.

379. Saxifraga hypnoides L.
Cut-leaved Saxifrage.

380. Saxifraga cæspitosa L.
Tufted Saxifrage.

381. Saxifraga granulata L.
Meadow Saxifrage.

382. Saxifraga cernua L.
Drooping Saxifrage.

383. Saxifraga rivularis L.
Brook Saxifrage.

384. Saxifraga tridactylites L.
Rue-leaved Saxifrage.

385. Saxifraga nivalis L.
Alpine Saxifrage.

386. Saxifraga stellaris L.
Star Saxifrage.

387. Saxifraga umbrosa L.
London Pride, St. Patrick's Cabbage ; Pk.

388. Saxifraga Geum L.
Kidney Saxifrage ; Pk.

389. Chrysosplenium oppositi-
folium L.

Golden Saxifrage ; Y.

390. Chrysosplenium alterni-
folium L.

Alternate-leaved Golden Saxifrage ; V.

391. Parnassia palustris L.

Grass of Parnassus.

XXXIII. DROSERACEÆ

392. Drosera rotundifolia L.

Common Sundew.

393. Drosera longifolia L.

Oblong Sundew.

2. *Calycifloræ*

394. Drosera anglica Huds.
English Sundew.

395. Myriophyllum spicatum L.
Spiked Water-Milfoil.

396. Myriophyllum verticillatum L.
Whorled Water-Milfoil.

397. Hippuris vulgaris L.
Marestai.

398. Hydrocotyle vulgaris L.
Marsh Penny-wort, White-rot.

399. Sanicula europæa L.
Sanicle.

400. Astrantia major L.
Astrantia.

401. Eryngium maritimum L.
Sea Holly; B.

402. Eryngium campestre L.
Field Eryngo; B.

403. Cicuta virosa L.
Cowbane, Water Hemlock.

404. Apium graveolens L.
Celery.

405. Apium nodiflorum Reichb.
Procumbent A.

406. Apium inundatum Reichb

Lesser A.

407. Sison Amomum L.

Hedge S., Bastard Stone Parsley.

408. Trinia glauca Dumort.

T. vulgaris DC.

Honewort.

409. Ægopodium Podagraria L.

Goutweed, Bishopweed, Herb Gerard.

410. Carum Petroselinum Benth.
Parsley; Y.

411. Carum segetum Benth.
Corn Parsley.

412 Carum verticillatum Koch.
Whorled Caraway.

413. Carum Carvi L.
Caraway.

414. Carum Bulbocastanum Koch.

Tuberous Caraway.

415. Sium latifolium L.

Water Parsnip.

416. Sium erectum Huds.

S. angustifolium·L.

Lesser Water-Parsnip.

417. Pimpinella Saxifraga L.

Burnet Saxifrage.

418. Pimpinella major Huds.
P. magna L.
Greater Burnet Saxifrage ; Pk.

419. Bupleurum rotundifolium L
Hare's-Ear, Thorow-wax ; Y.

420. Bupleurum opacum Lange.
B. aristatum Bartl.
Narrow Hare's-Ear ; Y.

421. Bupleurum tenuissimum L.
Slender Hare's-Ear ; Y

422. Bupleurum falcatum L.

Falcate Hare's-Ear; Y.

423. Œnanthe fistulosa L,

Water Dropwort.

424. Œnanthe pimpinelloides L.

Parsley Water Dropwort.

425. Œnanthe crocata L.

Hemlock Water Dropwort.

426. Œnanthe Phellandrium Lam.
Fine-leaved Water Dropwort.

427. Æthusa Cynapium L.
Fool's Parsley.

428. Fœniculum vulgare Mill.
Fennel; Y,

429. Seseli Libanotis Koch.
Mountain S,

430. Ligusticum scoticum L.
Lovage.

431. Silaus flavescens Bernh.
S. pratensis Bess.
Pepper Saxifrage; Y.

432. Meum athamanticum Jacq.
Spignel, Meu, Baldmoney; Pk.

433. Crithmum maritimum L.
Samphire.

434. Angelica sylvestris L.
Wild Angelica.

434a. Selinum carvifolia L.
Milk Parsley

435. Peucedanum officinale L.
Hog's Fennel, Sulphur-weed.

436. Peucedanum palustre Mœnch
Hog's Fennel, Milk Parsley.

437. Peucedanum Ostruthium Koch.

Master-wort.

438. Pastinaca sativa L.

Parsnip; Y.

439. Heracleum Sphondylium L

Cow Parsnip, Hogweed.

440. Tordylium maximum L.

Hartwort; Pk.

441. Scandix Pecten-Veneris L.
Shepherd's needle, Venus's comb.

442. Myrrhis Odorata Scop.
Sweet Cicely.

443. Conopodium denudatum
Koch.
Earthnut, Pignut.

444. Chærophyllum temulum L.
Rough Chervil.

445. Chærophyllum sylvestre L.
Wild Chervil.

**446. Chærophyllum Anthriscus
Crantz.**
Burr Chervil.

447. Caucalis nodosa Scop.
Knotted C.

448. Caucalis Anthriscus Huds.
Hedge Parsley.

449. Caucalis arvensis Huds.

Spreading C.

450. Caucalis daucoides L.

Small C.

451. Caucalis latifolia L.

Broad C.

452. Daucus Careta L.

Carrot.

453. Conium maculatum L.

Hemlock.

454. Danaa cornubiensis Burnat.

Physospermum cornubiense DC.

Cornish Blaader-seed.

455. Smyrnium Olusatrum L.

Alexanders; Y.

456. Coriandrum sativum L.

Coriander.

2. *Calycifloræ*

457. Hedera Helix L.

Ivy ; G.

458. Viscum album L.

Mistletoe G.

XXXVIII. CORNACEÆ

459. Cornus suecica L.

Dwarf Cornel ; P.

460. Cornus sanguinea L.

Dagwood.

461. Adoxa Moschatellina L.
Moschatel ; G.

462. Sambucus nigra L.
Common Elder

463. Sambucus Ebulus L.
Dwarf Elder, Danewort.

464. Viburnum Lantana L.
Wafaring Tree.

465. Viburnum Opulus L.

Guelder Rose.

466. Lonicera Periclymenum L.

Common Honeysuckle, Woodbine ; *Y.*

467. Lonicera Caprifolium L.

Perfoliate Honeysuckle ; *Y.*

468. Lonicera Xylosteum L.

Fly Honeysuckle.

469. Linnæa borealis L.

Linnæa ; Pk.

470. Rubia peregrina L.

Madder ; G

471 Galium Cruciata Scop.

Crosswort ; Y.

472. Galium verum L.

Ladies' Bedstraw ; Y.

473. Galium palustre L.

Marsh Bedstraw.

474. Galium uliginosum L.

Swamp Bedstraw.

475. Galium saxatile L.

Heath Bedstraw.

476. Galium Mollugo L.

Hedge Bedstraw.

477. Galium anglicum Huds.
Wall Bedstraw.

478. Galium boreale L.
Northern Bedstraw.

479. Galium Aparine L.
Cleavers, Goose-grass.

480. Galium tricorne With.
Corn Bedstraw.

481. **Asperula odorata** L.
Woodruff.

482. **Asperula cynanchica** L.
Squinancywort.

XLI. VALERIANACEÆ

483. **Sherardia arvensis** L.
Field Madder; B.

484. **Kentranthus ruber** DC.
Red Valerian.

485. Valeriana dioica L.
Marsh Valerian; R.

486. Valeriana officinalis L.
Common Valerian, All-heal.

487. Valeriana pyrenaica L.
Pyrenean Valerian.

488. Valerianella Locusta Betcke.
V. olitoria Poll.
Cornsalad, Lamb's-lettuce.

489. Valerianella carinata Lois.
Keeled Cornsalad.

490. Valerianella rimosa Bast.
V. Auricula DC.
Sharp-fruited Cornsalad

XLII. DIPSACACEÆ

491. Valerianella dentata Poll.
Narrow-fruited Cornsalad.

492. Dipsacus sylvestris L.
Wild Teasel; P.

493. Dipsacus pilosus L.

Small Teasel.

494. Scabiosa Succisa L.

Devil's-bit; B.

495. Scabiosa **Columbaria** L.

Small Scabious; B.

496. Scabiosa arvensis L.

Field Scabious; P.

497. Eupatorium cannabinum L.

Hemp Agrimony; P.

498. Aster Tripolium L.

Sea Aster; P

499. Aster Linosyris Bernh.

Goldilocks; Y.

500. Erigeron acris L.

Fleabane; P.

501   Erigeron alpinus L.
Alpine Fleabane; P.

502. Erigeron canadensis L.
Canadian Fleabane.

503. Solidago Virgaurea L.
Goldenrod; Y.

504. Bellis perennis L.
Daisy.

505. Filago germanica L.

Cudweed; Y.

506. Filago minima Pers.

Field Cudweed; Y.

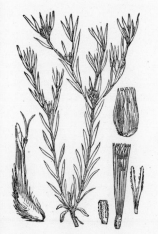

507. Filago gallica L.

Narrow Cudweed; Y.

508. Gnaphalium luteo-album L.

Jersey Cudweed; Y.

509. Gnaphalium sylvaticum L.
Wood Cudweed; Br.

511. Gnaphalium uliginosum L.
Marsh·Cudweed; Y.

510. Gnaphalium supinum L.
Dwarf Cudweed; Br.

512. Antennaria dioica Gaertn.
Mountain Everlasting, Cat's-ear.

513. Antennaria margaritacea Br.
Pearl Antennaria.

514. Inula Helenium L.
Elecampane; Y.

515. Inula salicina L.
Willow-leaved I.; Y.

516. Inula crithmoides L.
Golden Samphire; Y.

517. Inula Conyza DC.
Ploughman's Spikenard, Y.

518. Inula dysenterica L.

Fleabane I. ; Y.

519. Inula Pulicaria L.

Small Fleabane ; Y.

520. Xanthium Strumarium L.

Burweed ; G.

528. Bidens cernua L.

Bur-Marigold; Y.

522. Bidens tripartita L.

Three-cleft Bur-Marigold; Y.

523. Chrysanthemum Leucan-
themum L.

Ox-eye Daisy.

524. Chrysanthemum segetum L.

Corn Marigold; Y.

525. Chrysanthemum Parthenium
Pers.

Feverfew

526. Matricaria inodora L.
Scentless Matricary.

527. Matricaria Chamomilla L.
Wild Chamomile.

528. Anthemis Cotula L.
Stinking Mayweed.

529. Anthemis arvensis L.
Corn Chamomile.

530. Anthemis nobilis L.
Common Chamomile.

531. Anthemis tinctoria L.
Yellow Chamomile.

532. Achillea Ptarmica L.
Sneezewort.

533. Achillea Millefolium L.
Milfoil, Yarrow.

L

534. Diotis maritima Cass.

Cotton-Weed; Y.

535. Tanacetum vulgare L.

Tansy; Y.

536. Artemisia campestris L.

Field A.; Y.

537. Artemisia maritima L.

Sea A.; Y.

538. Artemisia vulgaris L.

Mugwort ; Y.

539. Artemisia Absinthium L.

Wormwood, Absinth ; Y.

540. Tussilago Farfara L.

Coltsfoot ; Y.

541. Tussilago Petasites L.

Butterbur ; P.

542. Senecio vulgaris L.

Groundsel; Y.

543. Senecio viscosus L.

Viscous S.; Y.

544. Senecis sylvaticus L.

Wood S.; Y.

545. Senecio squalidus L.

Squalid S ; Y.

546. Senecio aquaticus Huds.

Water S.; Y.

547. Senecio jacobæa L.

Ragwort; Y.

548. Senecio crucifolius L.

Narrow-leaved S.; Y.

549. Senecio paludosus L.

Fen S.; Y.

550. Senecio saracenicus L.

Broad-leaved S.; Y.

551. Senecio palustris Hook.

Marsh S.; Y.

552. Senecio campestris D.C.

Field S.; Y.

553. Doronicum Pardalianches L.

Leopard's-bane; Y.

554. Doronicum plantagineum L.
Plantain D.; Y.

555. Arctium Lappa L.
Burdock; P;

556. Serratula tinctoria L.
Sawwort, P.

557. Saussurea alpina DC.
Alpine S.; P.

558. Carduus Marianus L.

Milk Thistle; P.

559. Carduus nutans L.

Musk Thistle; P

560. Carduus crispus L.

C. acanthoides L.

Welted Thistle; P.

561. Carduus pycnocephalus L.

Slender Thistle; Pk., W.

562. Carduus lanceolatus L.
Spear Thistle; P.

563. Carduus palustris L.
Marsh Thistle; P.

564. Carduus arvensis Robs
Creeping Thistle; P.

565. Carduus eriophorus L.
Woolly Thistle; P.

566. Carduus heterophyllus L.
Melancholy Thistle ; *P.*

567. Carduus tuberosus L.
Tuberous Thistle; *P.*

568. Carduus pratensis Huds.
Meadow Thistle; *P.*

569. Carduus acaulis L.
Dwarf Thistle; *P.*

570. Onopordon Acanthium L.
Scotch or Cotton Thistle; P.

571. Carlina vulgaris L.
Carline Thistle; P.

572. Centaurea nigra L.
Knapweed, Hardheads; P.

573. Centaurea Scabiosa L.
Greater Knapweed; P.

574. Centaurea Cyanus L.

Bluebottle, Cornflower; B.

575. Centaurea aspera L.

Guernsey C.; P.

576. Centaurea Calcitrapa L.

Star Thistle; P.

577. Centaurea solstitialis L.

Yellow C.

578. Tragopogon pratensis L.

Goat's-beard; Y.

579. Tragopogon porrifolius L.

Purple Salsify.

580. Helminthia echioides Gærtn.

Ox-tongue; Y.

581. Picris hieracioides L.

Hawkweed P.; Y.

582. Leontodon hispidus L.
Common Hawkbit ; Y.

583. Leontodon autumnalis L.
Autumnal Hawkbit ; Y.

584. Leontodon hirtus L.
Lesser Hawkbit ; Y.

585. Hypochœris glabra L.
Glabrous Cat's-ear ; Y.

586. Hypochœris radicata L.
Cat's-ear; Y.

587. Hypochœris maculata L.
Spotted Cat's-ear; Y.

588. Lactuca muralis Gaertn.
Wall Lettuce; Y.

589. Lactuca Serriola L.
L. Scariola L.
Prickly Lettuce; Y.

590. Lactuca **saligna** L.
Willow Lettuce; Y.

591. Lactuca alpina Benth.
Alpine Lettuce; B.

592. Sonchus arvensis L.
Corn Sowthistle; Y.

593. Sonchus palustris L.
Marsh Sowthistle; Y.

594. **Sonchus oleraceus L.**

Common Sowthistle; Y.

595. **Taraxacum officinale Weber.**

T. Dens-leonis Desf.

Dandelion; Y.

596. **Crepis taraxacifolia Thuill.**

Beaked Hawk's-beard; Y.

597. **Crepis fœtida L.**

Fetid Hawk's-beard; Y.

598. Crepis capillaris Wallr

C. virens L.

Smooth Hawk's-beard; Y.

599. Crepis biennis L.

Rough Hawk's-beard; Y.

600. Crepis mollis Aschers.

C. hieracioides Jacq.

Soft Hawk's-beard; Y.

601. Crepis paludosa Mœnch.

Marsh Hawk's-beard; Y.

602. Hieracium Pilosella L.

Mouse-ear Hawkweed; Y.

603. Hieracium alpinum L

Alpine Hawkweed; Y.

604. Hieracium murorum L.

Wall Hawkweed; Y.

605. Hieracium cerinthoides L.

Honeywort Hawkweed; Y.

606. Hieracium umbellatum L.

Umbellate Hawkweed; Y.

607. Hieracium sabaudum L.

Savoy Hawkweed; Y.

608. Hieracium prenanthoides Vill.

Prenanth Hawkweed; Y.

609. Cichorium Intybus L.

Succory, Chicory; B.

610. Arnoseris minima Schw. &
Koerte.
A. pusilla Gærtn.
Lamb's or Swine's Succory; Y.

611. Lapsana communis L.
Nipplewort; Y.

XLIV. CAMPANULACEÆ

612. Lobelia Dortmanna L.
Water L.; B.

613. Lobelia urens L.
Acrid L.; B.

614. Jasione montana L.
Sheep's-bit ; B.

615. Phyteuma orbiculare L.
Round-headed Rampion ; B.

616. Phyteuma spicatum L.
Spiked Rampion ; B.

617. Campanula glomerata L.
Clustered C. ; B.

618. Campanula Trachelium L.

Nettle-leaved C.; B.

619. Campanula latifolia L.

Giant C.; B.

620. Campanula rapunculoides L.

Creeping C.; B.

621. Campanula Rapunculus L.

Rampion, Ramps; B.

622. Campanula patula L.

Spreading C.; P.

623. Campanula rotundifolia L.

Harebell; B.

624. Campanula hederacea L.

Ivy C.; B.-P.

625. Campanula hybrida L.

Corn C.; B.

626. Vaccinium Myrtillus L.
Bilberry, Blaeberry, Whortleberry.

1627. Vaccinium uliginosum L.
Bog Whortleberry.

628. Vaccinium Vitis-idæa L.
Red Whortleberry, Cowberry; Pk.

629. Vaccinium Oxycoccos L.
Cranberry; Pk.

630. Arbutus Unedo L.
Arbutus, Strawberry-tree.

631. Arctostaphylos Uva-ursi Spr.
Bearberry.

632. Arctostaphylos alpina Spr.
Black Bearberry.

633. Andromeda polifolia L.
Marsh A.; Pk.

634. Loiseleuria procumbens Desv.

Loiseleuria ; R

635. Menziesia polifolia Juss.

St. Dabeoc's Heath ; P.

636. Menziesia cærulea Sm.

Blue M.

637. Erica cinerea L.

Bell Heather ; P.

638. Erica Tetralix L.
Cross-leaved Heather; Pk.

639. Erica ciliaris L.
Ciliated Heather; R

640. Erica carnea L.
Mediterranean Heather; R.

641. Erica vagans L.
Cornish Heather; Pk.

642. Calluna vulgaris Salisb.
Ling; Pk.

643. Pyrola uniflora L.
One-flowered Wintergreen.

644. Pyrola rotundifolia L.
Larger Wintergreen.

645. Pyrola media Sw.
Intermediate Wintergreen.

646. Pyrola minor L.

Common Wintergreen.

647. Pyrola secunda L.

Serrated Wintergreen.

XLVI. PRIMULACEÆ

648. Monotropa Hypopithys L.

Yellow Bird's-nest.

649. Hottonia palustris L.

Water Violet, Featherfoil ; P.

650. **Primula vulgaris** Huds.

Primrose; Y.

651. **Primula veris** L.

Cowslip; Y.

652. **Primula farinosa** L.

Bird's-eye Primrose; Li.

653. **Cyclamen europæum** L.

Cyclamen, Sowbread; R.

654. Lysimachia **vulgaris** L.

Common Loosestrife ; Y.

655. Lysimachia thyrsiflora L.

Tufted L. ; **Y.**

656. Lysimachia Nummularia L.

Moneywort, Creeping Jenny ; Y.

657. Lysimachia nemorum L.

Wood L. ; Y.

658. Trientalis europæa L.

Trientale.

659. Glaux maritima L.

Sea Milkwort, Black Saltwort; Pk.

660. Anagallis arvensis L.

Pimpernel, Shepherd's or Poor Man's Weather-glass; B., R.

661. Anagallis tenella L.

Bog Pimpernel; Pk.

662. Centunculus minimus L.

Chaffweed ; Pk.

663. Samolus Valerandi L.

Brookweed.

XLVII. LENTIBULARIACEÆ

664. Pınguicula vulgaris L.

Common Butterwort ; P.

665. Pinguicula alpina L.

Alpine Butterwort ; Y.

666. Pinguicula lusitanica L.
Pale Butterwort ; Y.

667. Utricularia vulgaris L.
Common Bladderwort ; Y.

668. Utricularia minor L.
Lesser Bladderwort ; Y.

669. Utricularia intermedia Hayne.
Intermediate Bladderwort ; Y.

670. Fraxinus excelsior L.

Ash.

671. Ligustrum vulgare L.

Privet.

XLIX. APOCYNACEÆ

672. Vinca major L.

Larger Periwinkle; B.

673 Vinca minor L.

Lesser Periwinkle; B.

674. Cicendia filiformis Reichb.
Slender C.; Y.

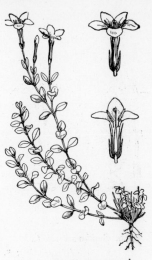

676a. Erythræa portensis Hoffm. & Lk.
Perennial Centaury; Pk.

675. Cicendia pusilla Gris.
Dwarf C.; Y.

676. Erythræa Centaurium Pers.
Common Centaury; Pk.

677. Gentiana Pneumonanthe L
Marsh Gentian; B.

678. Gentiana verna L.
Spring Gentian ; B.

679. Gentiana nivalis L.
Small Gentian ; B.

680. Gentiana Amarella L.
Felwort ; B.

681. Gentiana campestris L.
Field Gentian ; B.

682. Blackstonia perfoliata Huds.
Chlora perfoliata L.
Yellow-wort.

683. Menyanthes trifoliata L.
Buckbean, Marsh Trefoil.

LI. POLEMONIACEÆ

684. Limnanthemum nymphæoides Link.
Limnanthemum; Y.

685. Polemonium cæruleum L.
Greek Valerian, Jacob's Ladder; B.

686. Convolvulus arvensis L.

Lesser Bindweed; Pk., W.

687. Convolvulus sepium L.

Larger Bindweed.

688. Convolvulus Soldanella L.

Sea Bindweed; Pk.

689. Cuscuta europæa L.

Greater Dodder.

690. Cuscuta Epilinum Weihe.
Flax Dodder.

691. Cuscuta Epithymum L.
Lesser Dodder.

LIII. BORAGINACEÆ

692. Echium vulgare L.
Viper's Bugloss; B.

693. Echium plantagineum L.
Purple Viper's Bugloss.

694. Pulmonaria longifolia Boreau.

Lungwort; B.

695. Mertensia maritima S. F. Gray.

Sea Mertensia; B.

696. Lithospermum arvense L.

Corn Gromwell, Bastard Alkanet.

697. Lithospermum officinale L.

Common Gromwell.

698. Lithospermum purpureo-caeruleum L.

Creeping Gromwell ; B.

699. Myosotis scorpioides L.

M. palustris Hill.

Water Forget-me-not ; B.

700. Myosotis sylvatica Hoffm.

Wood Forget-me-not ; B.

701. Myosotis arvensis Hill.

Field Forget-me-not ; B.

702. Myosotis collina Hoffm.

Early Forget-me-not; B.

703. Myosotis versicolor Sm.

Yellow and Blue Forget-me-not.

704. Anchusa officinalis L.

Common Alkanet; B.

705. Anchusa sempervirens L.

Green Alkanet; B.

706. Lycopsis arvensis L.

Bugloss ; B.

707. Symphytum officinale L

Common Comfrey ; Y., R.,P.

708. Symphytum tuberosum L.

Tuberous Comfrey ; P.

709. Borago officinalis L.

Borage ; B.

710. Asperugo procumbens L.

Madwort ; B.

711. Cynoglossum officinale L.

Common Hound's-tongue ; R.

LIV. SOLANACEÆ

712. Cynoglossum montanum L.

Green Hound's-tongue ; P.

713. Datura Stramonium L.

Thorn-apple

714. Hyoscyamus niger L.

Henbane; Y.

715. Solanum Dulcamara L.

Bittersweet, Nightshade; B.

716. Solanum nigrum L.

Black Nightshade.

717. Atropa Belladonna L.

Dwale, Deadly Nightshade; P.

718. Orobanche major L.

Great Broomrape ; Br.

719. Orobanche caryophyllacea Sm.

Clove-scented Broomrape ; Br.

720. Orobanche rubra Sm.

Red Broomrape.

721. Orobanche elatior Sutt.

Tall Broomrape ; Y.-Br.

722. Orobanche minor Sm.
Lesser Broomrape; Br.

723. Orobanche purpurea Jacq.
O. cærulea Vill.
Blue Broomrape.

724. Orobanche ramosa L.
Branched Broomrape; B.

725. Lathræa squamaria L.
Toothwort.

726. Verbascum Thapsus L.
Great Mullein; Y.

727. Verbascum Blattaria L.
Moth Mullein; Y.

728. Verbascum virgatum Stokes.
Twiggy Mullein; Y.

729. Verbascum nigrum L.
Dark Mullein; Y.

730. Verbascum Lychnitis L.
White Mullein.

731. Verbascum pulverulentum Vill.
Hoary Mullein; Y.

732. Antirrhinum majus L.
Great Snapdragon; R.

733. Antirrhinum Orontium L.
Lesser Snapdragon; R.

734. Linaria vulgaris Mill.

Toadflax; Y.

735. Linaria repens Mill.

Pale Toadflax.

736. Linaria Pelisseriana Mill.

Pelisser's Toadflax; P.

737. Linaria supina Desf.

Supine Toadflax; Y.

738. Linaria minor Desf.
Lesser Toadflax; P.

739. Linaria Cymbalaria Mill.
Ivy-leaved Toadflax; L.

740. Linaria spuria Mill.
Male Fluellen; Y.

741. Linaria Elatine Mill.
Pointed-leaved Toadflax; Y.

742. Scrophularia nodosa L.
Figwort; G., P.-Br.

743. Scrophularia aquatica L.
Water Figwort; P.

744. Scrophularia Scorodonia L.
Balm-leaved Figwort; P.

745. Scrophularia vernalis L.
Yellow Figwort.

746. Mimulus guttatus DC.
M. luteus Willd.
Yellow M. ; Y.

747. Limosella aquatica L.
Mudwort ; R.

748. Sibthorpia europæa L.
Sibthorpia ; Y.

749. Digitalis purpurea L.
Foxglove ; P.

750. Veronica spicata L.
Spiked Speedwell ; B.

751. Veronica fruticans Jacq.
V. saxatilis L.
Rock Speedwell ; B.

752. Veronica alpina L.
Alpine Speedwell ; B.

753. Veronica serpyllifolia L.
Thyme-leaved Speedwell ; B.

754. Veronica officinalis L.

Common Speedwell; B.

755. Veronica Anagallis-
aquatica L.

Water Speedwell; B.

756. Veronica Beccabunga L.

Brooklime; B.

757. Veronica scutellata L.

Marsh Speedwell; B.

758. Veronica montana L.
Mountain Speedwell; B.

759. Veronica Chamædrys L.
Germander Speedwell; B.

760. Veronica hederæfolia L.
Ivy-leaved Speedwell; B.

761. Veronica agrestis L.
Procumbent Speedwell; B.

762. Veronica persica Poir.

V. Buxbaumii Ten.

Buxbaum's Speedwell ; B.

763. Veronica arvensis L.

Wall Speedwell ; B.

764. Veronica verna L.

Vernal Speedwell ; B.

765. Veronica triphyllos L.

Fingered Speedwell ; B.

766. Bartsia alpina L.

Alpine B. ; P.

767. Bartsia viscosa L.

Viscid B. ; Y.

768. Bartsia Odontites Huds.

Red B.

769. Euphrasia officinalis L.

Eyebright.

770. Rhinanthus Crista-galli L.
Yellow-Rattle; Y.

771. Pedicularis palustris L.
Red-Rattle; R.

772. Pedicularis sylvatica L.
Lousewort; R.

773. Melampyrum cristatum L.
Crested Cow-wheat; Y.

774. Melampyrum arvense L.

Purple Cow-wheat.

775. Melampyrum pratense L.

Common Cow-wheat ; Y

776. Melampyrum sylvaticum L.

Small-flowered Cow-wheat ; Y

LVII. LABIATÆ

777. Salvia pratensis L.

Meadow Sage ; B.

778. Salvia Verbenaca L.

Clary; B.

779. Lycopus europæus L.

Gipsywort.

780. Mentha longifolia Huds.

M. sylvestris L.

Horse Mint; Li.

781. Mentha rotundifolia Huds.

Round-leaved Mint; Pk.

782. **Mentha spicata** L.

M. viridis L.

Spear Mint ; Li.

783. **Mentha piperita** L.

Pepper Mint ; Li.

784. **Mentha aquatica** L.

Water Mint ; Li.

785. **Mentha sativa** L.

Whorled Mint ; Li.

786. Mentha arvensis L.
Corn Mint; Li.

787. Mentha Pulegium **L.**
Pennyroyal; Li.

788. Thymus Serpyllum L.
Wild Thyme; P.

789. Origanum vulgare L.
Marjoram; P.

790. Calamintha Acinos Clairv.
Basil-Thyme; P.

791. Calamintha officinalis Mœnch.
Calamint; P.

792. Calamintha vulgare Druce.
C. Clinopodium Benth.
Hedge Calamint, Wild Basil; P.

793. Nepeta hederacea Trev.
N. Glechoma Benth.
Ground-Ivy; B.

794. Nepeta Cataria L.

Catmint ; B.

795. Prunella vulgaris L.

Self-heal ; P.

795a. Prunella laciniata L.

Self-heal.

796. Scutellaria galericulata L.

Common Skullcap ; B.

797. Scutellaria minor L.
Lesser Skullcap; Pk.

798. Melittis Melissophyllum L.
Bastard Balm; Pk.

799. Marrubium vulgare L.
White Horehound.

800. Stachys officinalis Trev.
S. Betonica Benth.
Betony; P.

801. Stachys germanica L.

Downy Woundwort; P.

802. Stachys sylvatica L.

Hedge.Woundwort; P.

803. Stachys palustris L.

Marsh Woundwort; P.

804. Stachys arvensis L.

Field Woundwort; P.

805. Galeopsis Ladanum L.

Red Hemp-nettle; P.

806. Galeopsis dubia Leers.

G. ochroleuca Lam.

Downy Hemp-nettle; Y.

807. Galeopsis Tetrahit L.

Common Hemp-nettle; P.

808. Ballota nigra L.

Black Horehound; P.

809. **Leonurus Cardiaca** L.

Motherwort; Pk.

810. **Lamium amplexicaule** L.

Henbit; R.

811. **Lamium purpureum** L.

Red Dead-nettle.

812. **Lamium album** L.

White Dead-nettle.

813. Lamium maculatum L.

Spotted Dead-nettle; R.

814. Lamium Galeobdolon Crantz.

Yellow Archangel.

815. Teucrium Scorodonia L.

Wood-sage; Y.

816. Teucrium Scordium L.

Water Germander; R.

817. Teucrium Botrys L.

Cut-leaved Germander ; R.

818. Teucrium Chamædrys L.

Wall Germander ; R.

819. Ajuga reptans L.

Common Bugle ; B.

820. Ajuga pyramidalis L.

A. genevensis L.

Erect Bugle ; B.

LVIII. VERBENACEÆ
I. *Dicotyledons*

821. Ajuga Chamæpitys Schreb.
Ground Pine ; Y.

822. Verbena officinalis L.
Vervain.

LIX. PLUMBAGINACEÆ

823. Statice Limonium L.
Common Sea Lavender ; P.

824. Statice binervosa G. E. Sm.
S. auriculæfolia Vahl.
Rock Sea Lavender ; P.

825. Statice bellidifolia DC.
S. reticulata L.
Matted Sea Lavender.

826. Armeria maritima Willd.
A. vulgaris Willd.
Thrift, Sea Pink.

LX. PLANTAGINACEÆ

827. Armeria plantaginea Willd.
Plantain Thrift; Pk.

828. Plantago major L.
Greater Plantain.

829. Plantago media L.
Hoary Plantain.

830. Plantago lanceolata L.
Ribwort.

831. Plantago maritima L.
Sea Plantain.

832. Plantago Coronopus L.
Bucks-horn Plantain.

834. Corrigiola littoralis L.

Strapwort.

833. Littorella uniflora Aschers.

L. lacustris L.

Shore-weed.

835. Herniaria glabra L.

Rupture-wort ; G.

837. Scleranthus annuus L.

Annual Knawel ; G.

836. Illecebrum verticillatum L.

Illecebrum.

838. Scleranthus perennis L.
Perennial Knawel; G.

839. Salicornia herbacea L.
Marsh Samphire, Glasswort.

840. Suæda fruticosa Dum.
Shrubby Seablite; G.

841. Suæda maritima Dum.
Herbaceous Seablite; G.

842. Salsola Kali L.
Saltwort.

843. Chenopodium Vulvaria L.
Stinking Goosefoot; G.

844. Chenopodium polyspermum L.
Many-seeded Goosefoot; G.

845. Chenopodium album L.
White Goosefoot, Fat Hen; G.

846. Chenopodium glaucum L.
Glaucous Goosefoot ; G.

847. Chenopodium rubrum L.
Red Goosefoot.

848. Chenopodium urbicum L.
Upright Goosefoot ; G.

849. Chenopodium murale L.
Nettle-leaved Goosefoot ; G.

850. Chenopodium hybridum L.
Sowbane ; G.

851. Chenopodium Bonus-
Henricus L.
Good King Henry, Allgood ; G.

852. Beta maritima L.
Wild Beet ; G.

853. Atriplex portulacoides L.
Sea Purslane.

854. Atriplex pedunculata L.
Stalked Orache.

855. Atriplex hortensis L.
Garden Orache.

856. Atriplex patula L.
Common Orache.

857. Atriplex sabulosa Rouy.
A. rosea L.

Frosted Orache.

858. Rumex longifolius DC.
R. aquaticus L.
Smooth-fruited Dock.

859. Rumex crispus L.
Curled Dock.

860. Rumex obtusifolius L.
Broad Dock.

861. Rumex Hydrolapathum Huds.
Water Dock.

862. Rumex conglomeratus Murr.

Clustered Dock.

863. Rumex nemorosus Schrader.

R. sanguineus L.

Red-veined Dock.

864. Rumex pulcher L.

Fiddle Dock.

865. Rumex maritimus L.

Golden Dock.

866. Rumex Acetosa L.

Sorrel.

867. Rumex Acetosella L.

Sheep's-sorrel.

868. Oxyria digyna Hill.

O. reniformis Hook.

Mountain Sorrel.

869. Polygonum aviculare L.

Knotweed, Knotgrass.

870. Polygonum maritimum L.

Sea P.

871. Polygonum Convolvulus L.

Black Bindweed.

872. Polygonum dumetorum L.

Copse P.

873. Polygonum viviparum L.

Viviparous P.

874. Polygonum Bistorta L

Bistort, Snakeweed ; Pk.

875. Polygonum amphibium L.

Amphibious P. ; R.

876. Polygonum Persicaria L.

Persicaria ; R.

877. Polygonum lapathifolium L.

Pale P.

878. Polygonum Hydropiper L.

Waterpepper.

879. Polygonum minus Huds.

Slender P.

LXIV. THYMELEACEÆ

880. Daphne Mezereum L.

Mezereon; P.

881. Daphne Laureola L.

Spurge Laurel; G.

882. Hippophae rhamnoides L.
Sallow-thorn, Sea Buckthorn; G.

883. Thesium humifusum DC.
T. linophyllum L.
Bastard Toadflax.

LXVII. ARISTOLOCHIACEÆ

LXVIII. EUPHORBIACEÆ

884. Asarum europæum L.
Asarabacca; Br.

885. Euphorbia Peplis L.
Purple Spurge; G.

886. Euphorbia Helioscopia L.

Sun Spurge; G.

887. Euphorbia platyphyllos L.

Broad Spurge; G.

888. Euphorbia hiberna L.

Irish Spurge; G.

889. Euphorbia pilosa L.

Hairy Spurge; G.

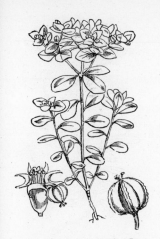

890. Euphorbia Peplus L.
Petty Spurge; G.

891. Euphorbia exigua L.
Dwarf Spurge; G.

892. Euphorbia Lathyrus L.
Caper Spurge; G.

893. Euphorbia segetalis L.
Portland Spurge; G.

894. Euphorbia Paralias L.
Sea Spurge ; G.

895. Euphorbia Esula L.
Leafy Spurge ; G.

896. Euphorbia amygdaloides L.
Wood Spurge ; G.

897. Mercurialis perennis L.
Dog's Mercury ; G.

898. Mercurialis annua L.

Annual Mercury ; G.

899. Buxus sempervirens L.

Box ; G.

LXIX. EMPETRACEÆ

LXX. CALLITRICHACEÆ

900. Empetrum nigrum L.

Crowberry.

901. Ceratophyllum demersum L.

Hornwort.

902. Callitriche aquatica Sm.
Water Starwort.

903. Urtica urens L.
Small Nettle; G.

904. Urtica pilulifera L.
Roman Nettle; G.

905. Urtica dioica L.
Common Nettle; G.

906. **Parietaria officinalis L.**
Pellitory; G.

907. **Humulus Lupulus L.**
Hop; G.

LXXII.   ULMACEÆ

908. **Ulmus glabra Huds.**
U. montana Stokes.
Scotch or Wych Elm; R.

909. **Ulmus campestris L.**
English Elm; R.

910. Myrica Gale L.
Sweet Gale, Bog Myrtle.

911. Alnus glutinosa Gaertn.
Alder.

912. Betula alba L.
Common Birch.

913. Betula nana L.
Dwarf Birch.

914. Carpinus Betulus L.
Hornbeam.

915. Corylus Avellana L.
Hazel Nut

916. Fagus sylvatica L.
Beech.

917. Quercus Robur L.
British ak

R

918. Salix pentandra L.

Bay Willow.

919. Salix fragilis L

Crack Willow.

920. Salix alba L.

White or Common Willow.

921. Salix triandra L.

S. amygdalina L.

Almond or French Willow.

922. **Salix purpurea** L.
Purple Willow.

923. **Salix viminalis** L.
Osier.

924. **Salix Caprea** L.
Sallow, Goat Willow.

925. **Salix aurita** L.
Round-eared Willow.

926. Salix phylicifolia L.
Tea-leaved Willow.

927. Salix repens L.
Creeping Willow.

928. Salix Lapponum L.
Downy Willow.

929. Salix lanata L.
Woolly Willow.

930. Salix Myrsinites L.
    Whortle Willow.

931. Salix reticulata L.
    Reticulate Willow.

932. Salix herbacea L.
    Dwarf Willow.

933. Populus alba L.
    White Poplar, Abele.

934. Populus tremula L.

Aspen.

935. Populus nigra L.

Black or Italian Poplar.

LXXIV. CONIFERÆ

(*Gymnosperms*)

936. Pinus sylvestris L.

Scotch Fir.

937. Juniperus communis L.

Juniper.

938. **Taxus** baccata L.
Yew ; G.

939. **Typha latifolia** L.
Great Reedmace, Cat's-tail ; Y.

940. **Typha angustifolia** L.
Lesser Reedmace ; Y.

941. **Sparganium erectum** L.
S. ramosum Huds.
Branched Bur-reed ; G.

942. Sparganium simplex Huds.
Simple Bur-reed; G.

943. Sparganium minimum Fries.
Small Bur-reed; G.

LXXVI. ARACEÆ

944. Arum maculatum L.
Cuckoo-pint,
Wake Robin, Lords-and-Ladies; Y., P.

945. Acorus Calamus L.
Sweet Flag, Sweet Sedge; Y.G.

II. *Monocotyledons*

946. Lemna trisulca L.
Ivy-leaved Duckweed.

947. Lemna minor L.
Lesser Duckweed.

948. Lemna gibba L.
Gibbous Duckweed.

949. Lemna polyrrhiza L.
Greater Duckweed.

950. Lemna arrhiza L.
Rootless Duckweed.

951. Zostera marina L.
Grass-wrack.

952. Zostera nana Roth.
Dwarf Grass-wrack.

953. Naias flexilis Rostk.

Slender N.

954. Naias marina L.

Holly-leaved N.

955. Naias graminea Del.

Grassy N.

956. Zannichellia palustris L.

Horned Pondweed.

957. Ruppia maritima L.
Sea R.

958. Potamogeton natans L.
Broad Pondweed.

959. Potamogeton heterophyllus Schreb.
Various-leaved Pondweed.

960. Potamogeton lucens L.
Shining Pondweed

961. Potamogeton prælongus Wulf.

Long Pondweed.

962. Potamogeton perfoliatus L.

Perfoliate Pondweed.

963. Potamogeton crispus L.

Curly Pondweed.

964. Potamogeton densus L

Opposite Pondweed.

965. Potamogeton obtusifolius
M. & K.
Obtuse Pondweed.

966. Potamogeton acutifolius Link.
Acute Pondweed.

967. **Potamogeton pusillus L.**
Slender Pondweed.

968. Potamogeton pectinatus L.
Fennel Pondweed.

969. Scheuchzeria palustris L.
Marsh S.

970. Triglochin palustre L.
Marsh Arrow-grass.

LXXIX. ALISMACEÆ

971. Triglochin maritimum L.
Sea Arrow-grass.

972. Butomus umbellatus L.
Flowering Rush; R.

973. Sagittaria sagittifolia L.
Arrowhead.

974. Alisma Plantago-aquatica L.
Common Water Plantain; R.

975. Alisma ranunculoides L.
Lesser Water Plantain; R.

976. Alisma natans L.
Floating Water Plantain

977. Damasonium Alisma Mill.
D. stellatum Pers.
Star-fruit.

978. Elodea canadensis Michx.
Water-thyme.

978a. Hydrilla verticillata Presl.
ydrilla.

979. Hydrocharis Morsus-ranæ L.
Frogbit.

980. Stratiotes Aloides L.
Water-soldier.

981. Malaxis paludosa Sw.
Bog Orchis; G.

982. Liparis Loeselii Rich.
Fen Orchis; G.

983. Corallorhiza trifida Chatel.
C. innata Br.
Coralroot; G.

984. **Epipactis Helleborine Crantz.**
E. latifolia All.
Broad Helleborine ; G.

985. **Epipactis palustris Crantz.**
Marsh Helleborine.

986. **Cephalanthera latifolia Janch.**
C. pallens Rich.
White Helleborine.

987. **Cephalanthera longifolia Fritsch.**
C. ensifolia Rich.
Narrow Helleborine.

988. Cephalanthera rubra Rich.
Red Helleborine.

989. Listera ovata Br.
Common Twayblade; G.

990. Listera cordata Br.
Lesser Twayblade; G.

991. Neottia Nidus-avis L.
Bird's-nest Orchis; Br.

992. Epipogum Gmelini Rich.
E. aphyllum Sw.
Leafless E. ; Y.

993. Spiranthes spiralis Koch.
S. autumnalis Rich.
Lady's Tresses.

994. Spiranthes æstivalis Rich.
Summer Lady's Tresses.

995. Spiranthes Romanzoffiana Cham.
Drooping Lady's Tresses.

996. Goodyera repens Br.
Creeping G.

997. Orchis Morio L.
Green-winged O.; P.

998. Orchis militaris L.
Military O.; P.

999. Orchis ustulata L.
Dwarf O.; P.

1000. Orchis mascula L.

Early Purple O.

1001. Orchis laxiflora Lam.

Loose O.; R.

1002. Orchis maculata L.

Spotted O.; Pk.

1003. Orchis latifolia L.

Marsh O.; Pk.

1004. Orchis hircina Crantz.

Lizard O.; G.

1005. Orchis pyramidalis L.

Pyramidal O.; R.

1006. Habenaria bifolia Br.

Butterfly Orchis.

1007. Habenaria conopsea L.

Fragrant Orchis; R.

1008. Habenaria intacta Benth.
Dense-spiked Orchis; Pk.

1009. Habenaria albida Br.
Small Orchis.

1010. Habenaria viridis Br.
Frog Orchis; G.

1011. Aceras anthropophora Br.
Man Orchis; G.

1012. Herminium Monorchis Br.
Musk Orchis; G.

1013. Ophrys apifera Huds.
Bee Orchis; Pk.

1014. Ophrys sphegodes Mill.
O. aranifera Huds.
Spider Orchis; Br.

1015. Ophrys muscifera Huds.
Fly Orchis; P.-Br

1016. Cypripedium Calceolus L.
Lady's Slipper ; V.

1017. Iris Pseudacorus L.
Yellow I., Yellow Flag.

1018. Iris fœtidissima L.
Fetid I., Gladdon, Roastbeef-plant ; V

1019. Gladiolus communis L.
Gladiolus ; R.

1020. Sisyrinchium angustifolium Mill.

Blue-eyed Grass.

1021. Romulea parviflora Britten.

R. Columnæ S. & M.

Romulea; B.

1022. Crocus vernus Mill.

Spring or Purple C.

1023. Crocus nudiflorus Sm.

Autumnal C.; P.

1024. Narcissus Pseudo-narcissus L.
Daffodil, Daffy-down-dilly, Lent Lily ; Y.

1025. Narcissus biflorus Curt.
Primrose Peerless.

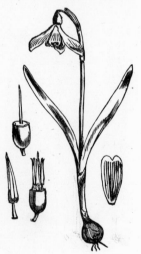

1026. Galanthus nivalis L.
Snowdrop.

1027. Leucoium æstivum L.
Summer Snowflake.

II. *Monocotyledons*

1028. Tamus communis L.

Black Bryony ; G.

1029. Paris quadrifolia L.

Herb-Paris ; G.

1030. Polygonatum verticillatum
Mœnch.

Whorled Solomon's Seal.

1031. Polygonatum multiflorum
Mœnch.

Common Solomon's Seal.

1032. Polygonatum anceps Mœnch.
P. officinale Mœnch.
Angular Solomon's Seal.

1033. Convallaria majalis L.
Lily of the Valley.

1034. Maianthemum bifolium Schmidt.
M. Convallaria Roth.
May Lily.

1035. Asparagus officinalis L.
Asparagus.

1036. Ruscus aculeatus L.
Butcher's Broom.

1037. Fritillaria Meleagris L.
Fritillary, Snake's-head; R.

1038. Tulipa sylvestris L.
Wild Tulip; Y.

1039. Lloydia serotina Reichb.
Mountain L.

1040. Gagea lutea Ker.

Yellow G.

1041. Ornithogalum umbellatum L.

Star of Bethlehem.

1042. Ornithogalum nutans L.

Drooping O.

1043. Ornithogalum pyrenaicum L.

Spiked O.

1044. Scilla verna Huds.
Spring Squill ; B.

1045. Scilla autumnalis L.
Autumnal Squill ; B.

1046. Scilla nonscripta Hoffm. & Lk.
S. nutans Sm.
Bluebell.

1047. Muscari racemosum DC.
Grape Hyacinth ; B.

T

1048. Allium Ampeloprasum L.

Wild Leek ; P.

1049. Allium Scorodoprasum L.

Sand Leek ; P.

1050. Allium oleraceum L.

Field Garlic ; Br.

1051. Allium Schœnoprasum L.

Chives ; P.

1052. Allium sphærocephalum L.
Round-headed Leek ; P.

1053. Allium vineale L.
Crow Garlic ; P.

1054. Allium ursinum L.
Ramsons.

1055. Allium triquetrum L.
Triquetrous Leek.

**1056. Simethis planifolia
Gren. & Godr.**

S. bicolor Kunth.

Variegated S.

1057. Narthecium ossifragum Huds.

Bog Asphodel ; Y.

1058. Tofieldia borealis Wahl.

T. palustris Huds.

Scottish Asphodel ; G.

1059. Colchicum autumnale L.

Meadow Saffron ; R

1060. Juncus commuis Mey.
Common Rush.

1061. Juncus glaucus Ehrh.
Hard Rush.

1062. Juncus filformis L.
Thread Rush.

1063. Juncus balticus Willd.
Baltic Rush.

1064. Juncus articulatus L.
Jointed Rush.

1065. Juncus obtusiflorus Hoffm.
Obtuse Rush.

1066. Juncus compressus Jacq.
Round-fruited Rush.

1067. Juncus tenuis Willd.
Slender Rush.

1068. Juncus squarrosus L.

Heath Rush.

1069. Juncus bufonius L.

Toad Rush.

1070. Juncus pygmæus Rich.

Dwarf Rush.

1071. Juncus capitatus Weig.

Capitate Rush.

1072. Juncus maritimus Lam.

Sea Rush.

1073. Juncus acutus L.

Sharp Rush.

1074. Juncus trifidus L.

Highland Rush.

1075. Juncus castaneus Sm.

Chestnut Rush.

1076. Juncus biglumis L.
Two-flowered Rush.

1077. Luzula pilosa Willd.
Hairy Woodrush.

1078. Luzula sylvatica Gaud.
Great Woodrush.

1079. Luzula arcuata Hook.
Curved Woodrush.

1080. Luzula campestris Br.
Field Woodrush.

1081. Luzula spicata DC.
Spiked Woodrush.

LXXXVII. ERIOCAULACEÆ

1082. Eriocaulon septangulare
With.
Pipe-Wort.

LXXXVIII. CYPERACEÆ

1083. Cyperus longus L.
Galingale.

1084. Cyperus fuscus L.

Brown C.

1085. Schœnus nigricans L.

Bog-rush.

1086. Schœnus ferrugineus L.

Ferruginous S.

1087. Cladium Mariscus Pohl.

Common Sedge.

1088. Rhynchospora fusca L.
Brown Beak-Sedge.

1089. Rhynchospora alba Vahl.
White Beak-Sedge.

1090. Blysmus compressus Panz.
Broad B.

1091. Blysmus rufus Link.
Narrow B.

1092. Scirpus acicularis'L.

Needle S.

1093. Scirpus parvulus R. & S

Small S.

1094. Scirpus palustris L.

Creeping S.

1095. Scirpus multicaulis Sm.

Many-stalked S.

1096. Scirpus pauciflorus Lightf.

Few-flowered S.

1097. Scirpus cæspitosus L.

Tufted S.

1098. Scirpus fluitans L.

Floating S.

1099. Scirpus setaceus L.

Bristle S.

1100. Scirpus cernuus Vahl.

S. Savii S. & M.

1101. Scirpus Holoschœnus L.

Clustered S.

1102. Scirpus americanus Pers.

S. pungens Vahl.

Sharp S.

1103. Scirpus triqueter L.

Triangular S.

1104. Scirpus lacustris L.

Bulrush.

1105. Scirpus maritimus L.

Sea S.

1106. Scirpus sylvaticus L.

Wood S.

1107. Eriophorum alpinum L.

Alpine Cotton-grass.

1108. Eriophorum vaginatum L.
Sheathing Cotton-grass.

1109. Eriophorum polystachion L.
Common Cotton-grass.

1110. Kobresia caricina Willd.
Kobresia.

1111. Carex dioica L.
Diœcious Sedge.

U

1112. Carex pulicaris L.
Flea Sedge.

1113. Carex rupestris All.
Rock Sedge.

1114. Carex pauciflora Lightf.
Few-flowered Sedge.

1114*a*. Carex microglochin Wahl.

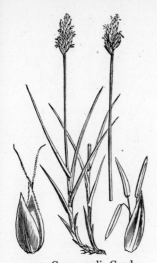

1115. Carex ovalis Good.

C. leporina L.

Oval Sedge.

1116. Carex lagopina Wahl.

Hare's-foot Sedge,

1117. Carex elongata L.

Elongated Sedge.

1118. Carex echinata Murr.

Star-headed Sedge.

1119. Carex canescens L.

Whitish Sedge.

1120   Carex remota L.

Remote Sedge

1121. Carex axillaris Good.

Axillary Sedge,

1122. Carex paniculata L.

Panicled Sedge.

1123. Carex vulpina L.

Fox Sedge.

1124. Carex spicata Huds.
C. muricata Good.

Prickly Sedge.

1125. Carex arenaria L.

Sand Sedge.

1126. Carex divisa Huds.

Divided Sedge.

1127. Carex incurva Lightf.
Curved Sedge.

1128. Carex saxatilis L.
Russet Sedge.

1129. Carex cæspitosa L.
Tufted Sedge.

1130. Carex acuta L.
Acute Sedge.

1131. Carex alpina Sw.

Alpine Sedge.

1132. Carex polygama Schkuhr.

C. Buxbaumii Wahl.

1133. Carex atrata L.

Black Sedge.

1134. Carex humilis Leyss.

Dwarf Sedge.

1135. Carex digitata L.

Fingered Sedge.

1136. Carex caryophyllea Latour.

C. præcox Jacq.

Vernal Sedge.

1137. Carex montana L.

Mountain Sedge.

1138. Carex pilulifera L.

Pill-headed Sedge.

1139. Carex tomentosa L.
Downy Sedge.

1140. Carex lasiocarpa Ehrh.
C. filiformis L.
Slender Sedge.

1141. Carex hirta L.
Hairy Sedge.

1142. Carex pallescens L.
Pale Sedge.

1143. Carex extensa Good.

Long-bracted Sedge.

1144. Carex flava L.

Yellow Sedge.

1145. Carex distans L.

Distant Sedge.

1146. Carex punctata Good

Dotted Sedge.

1147. Carex panicea L.
Carnation Sedge, Carnation-grass.

1148. Carex capillaris L.
Capillary Sedge.

1149. Carex limosa L.
Mud Sedge.

1150. Carex flacca Schreb.
C. glauca Murr.
Glaucous Sedge

1151. Carex sylvatica Huds.

Wood Sedge.

1152. Carex strigosa Huds.

Thin-spiked Sedge.

1153. Carex Pseudocyperus L.

Cyperus-like Sedge.

1154. Carex pendula Huds.

Pendulous Sedge.

1155. Carex rostrata Stokes.
C. ampullacea Good.
Bottle Sedge.

1156. Carex vesicaria L.
Bladder Sedge.

LXXXIX. GRAMINEÆ

1157. Carex acutiformis Ehrh.
C. paludosa Good.
Marsh Sedge.

1158. Leersia oryzoides Sw.
Leersia

1159. Milium effusum L.

Spreading M.

1160. Panicum sanguinale L.

Fingered P.

1161. Panicum humifusum Kunth.

P. glabrum Gaud.

Glabrous P.

1162. Panicum verticillatum L.

Rough P.

1163. Panicum glaucum L.

Glaucous P.

1164. Panicum viride L.

Green P

1165. Panicum Crus-galli L.

Cockspur P.

1166. Hierochloe odorata Wahl.

H. borealis R. & S.

Holy Grass.

1167. Anthoxanthum odoratum L.
Vernal Grass.

1168. Phalaris canariensis L.
Canary Grass.

1169. Digraphis arundinacea Trin.
Reed Grass.

1170. Phleum pratense L.
Timothy Grass, Cat's-tail.

1171. Phleum alpinum L.
Alpine Cat's-tail Grass.

1172. Phleum phleoides Simonk.
P. Bœhmeri Wibel.
Bœhmer's Cat's-tail Grass.

1173. Phleum arenarium L.
Sand Cat's-tail Grass.

1174. Alopecurus myosuroides Huds.
A. agrestis L.
Slender Foxtail.

X

1175. Alopecurus pratensis L.
        Meadow Foxtail.

1176. Alopecurus geniculatus L.
        Marsh Foxtail.

1177. Alopecurus alpinus Sm.
      Alpine Foxtail.

1178. Mibora minima Desv.
    M. verna Adans.
             Mibora.

1179. Lagurus ovatus L.
Hare's-tail.

1180. Polypogon monspeliensis Dest.
Annual Beardgrass.

1181. Polypogon littoralis Sm.
Perennial Beardgrass.

1182. Agrostis palustris Huds.
A. alba L.
Fiorin-grass.

1183. Agrostis canina L.

Brown-grass.

1184. Agrostis setacea Curt.

Bristle A.

1185. Agrostis Spica-venti L.

Silky A.

1186. Gastridium lendigerum Beauv.

Nitgrass.

1187. Psamma arenaria Beauv.
Maram, Sea Matweed.

1188. Calamagrostis epigeios Roth.
Bushgrass.

1189. Calamagrostis canescens Gmel.
C. lanceolata Roth.
Purple Smallreed.

1190. Calamagrostis stricta Koeler.
Narrow Smallreed.

1191. Aira cæspitosa L.

Tufted A.

1192. Aira flexuosa L.

Wavy A.

1193. Aira canescens L.

Grey A.

1194. Aira præcox L.

Early A.

1195. Aira caryophyllea L.

Silvery A., Hair-grass.

1196. Avena fatua L.

Wild Oat.

1197. Avena pratensis L.

Perennial Oat.

1198. Avena flavescens L.

Yellow Oat.

1199. Arrhenatherum elatius
M. & K.
A. avenaceum Beauv.
False Oat.

1200. Holcus lanatus L.
Yorkshire Fog.

1201. Holcus mollis L.
Soft H.

1202. Cynodon Dactylon Pers.
Bermuda Grass.

1203. Spartina stricta Sm.
Cordgrass.

1204. Lepturus incurvatus Trin.
Curved L.

1205. Nardus stricta L.
Matgrass.

1206. Elymus arenarius L.
Lymegrass.

1207. Hordeum europæum All.

H. sylvaticum Huds.

Wood Barley.

1208. Hordeum nodosum L.

H. pratense Huds.

Meadow Barley.

1209. Hordeum murinum L.

Wall Barley.

1210. Hordeum marinum Huds.

H. maritimum With.

Squirrel-tail Grass.

1211. Agropyrum repens Beauv.
Couch or Quitch.

1212. Agropyrum caninum Beauv.
Fibrous A.

1213. Lolium perenne L.
Ryegrass.

1214. Lolium temulentum L.
Darnel.

1215. Brachypodium sylvaticum
Beauv.
Slender False-brome.

1216. Brachypodium pinnatum L.
Heath False-brome.

1217. Bromus erectus Huds.
Upright Brome-grass.

1218. Bromus ramosus Huds.
B. asper Murr.
Hairy Brome-grass.

1219. Bromus sterilis L.
Barren Brome-grass.

1220. Bromus maximus Desf.
Great Brome-grass.

1221. Bromus madritensis L.
Compact Brome-grass.

1222. Bromus arvensis L.
Field Brome-grass.

1223. Bromus giganteus L.
Tall Brome-grass.

1224. Festuca ovina L.
Sheep's Fescue.

1225. Festuca elatior L.
Meadow Fescue.

1226. Festuca sylvatica Vill.
Reed Fescue.

1227. Festuca Myuros L.
Rat's-tail Fescue.

1228. Festuca membranacea Druce.
F. uniglumis Sol.
One-glumed Fescue.

1229. Dactylis glomerata L.
Cock's-foot Grass.

1230. Cynosurus cristatus L.
Crested Dog's-tail.

1231. Cynosurus echinatus L.
Rough Dog's-tail.

1232. Briza media L.
Common Quaking-grass.

1233. Briza minor L.
Lesser Quaking-grass.

1234. Poa aquatica L.

Reed P.

1235. Poa fluitans Scop.
Flote-grass.

1236. Poa Maritima Huds.
Sea P.

1237. Poa distans L.
Reflexed P.

1238. Poa rupestris With.
P. procumbens Curt.
Procumbent P.

Y

1239. Poa rigida L.

Hard P.

1240. Poa loliacea Huds.

Darnel P.

1241. Poa annua L.

Annual P.

1242. Poa compressa L.

Flattened P.

1243. Poa pratensis L.
Meadow-grass.

1244. Poa trivialis L.
Roughish Meadow-grass.

1245. Poa nemoralis L.
Wood P.

1246. Poa laxa Hænke.
Wavy P.

1247. Poa alpina L.

Alpine P.

1248. Poa bulbosa L.

Bulbous P.

1249. Catabrosa aquatica Beauv.

Water Catabrosa.

1250. Molinia cærulea Mœnch.

Purple M.

1251. Melica nutans L.
Mountain Melick.

1252. Melica uniflora Retz.
Wood Melick.

1253. Triodia decumbens Beauv.
Decumbent T.

1254. Kœleria cristata Pers.
Crested K.

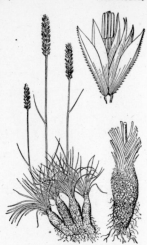

1255. Kœleria Vallesiana
Bertol.

1256. Sesleria cærulea Ard.

Blue S.

XC. LYCOPODIACEÆ
Cryptogams

1257. Arundo Phragmites L.
Common Reed.

1258. Lycopodium clavatum L.

Common Clubmoss.

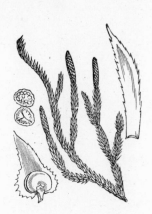

1259. Lycopodium annotinum L.
Interrupted Clubmoss.

1260. Lycopodium alpinum L.
Alpine Clubmoss.

1261. Lycopodium Selago L.
Fir Clubmoss.

1262. Lycopodium inundatum L.
Marsh Clubmoss.

**1263. Selaginella selaginoides
Gray.**

Lesser Clubmoss.

1264. Isoetes lacustris L.

Quillwort.

XCIII. MARSILIACEÆ

1265. Isoetes Hystrix Bory.

Quillwort.

1266. Pilularia globulifera L.

Creeping Pillwort.

67. Azolla filiculoides
Lam.

Azolla.

1268. Equisetum Telmateia
Ehrh.

Great Horse-tail.

1269. Equisetum arvense L.

Common Horse-tail.

1270. Equisetum sylvaticum L.

Wood Horse-tail.

1271. Equisetum pratense Ehrh.

Shady Horse-tail.

1272. Equisetum limosum L.
Smooth Horse-tail.

1273. Equisetum littorale Kühl.
Bog Horse-tail.

1274. Equisetum palustre L.
Marsh Horse-tail.

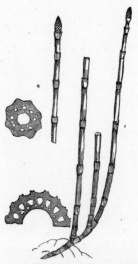

1275. Equisetum hyemale L.
Rough Horse-tail, Dutch Rush.

1276. Equisetum trachyodon
A. Braun.
Long Horse-tail.

1277. Equisetum variegatum
Schleich.
Variegated Horse-tail.

XCVI. OPHIOGLOSSACEÆ.
Filices

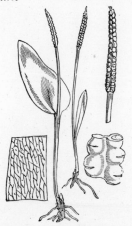

1278. Ophioglossum vulgatum L.
Adder's-tongue.

1279. Botrychium Lunaria Sw.
Moonwort.

1280. Osmunda regalis L.
Fern Royal.

1281. Polypodium vulgare L.
Common Polypody.

1282. Polypodium Phegopteris L.
Beech Fern.

1283. Polypodium alpestre Hoope.
Alpine Polypody.

1284. Polypodium Dryopteris L.
Oak Fern.

1285. Allosorus crispus Bernh.
Rock Bracken, Parsley Fern.

1286. Gymnogramme leptophylla
Desv.
Grammitis leptophylla Sw.
Small G.

1287. Aspidium Lonchitis Sw.
Holly Fern.

1288. Aspidium aculeatum Sw.

Prickly Shieldfern.

1289. Aspidium Thelypteris Sw.

Marsh Shieldfern.

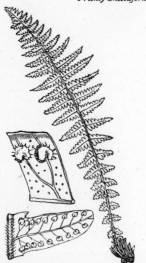

1290. Aspidium Oreopteris Sw.

Mountain Shieldfern.

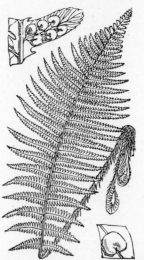

1291. Aspidium Filix-mas Sw.

Male Fern.

1292. Aspidium cristatum Sw.
Crested Shieldfern.

1293. Aspidium spinulosum Sw.
Broad Shieldfern.

1294. Aspidium rigidum Sw.
Rigid Shieldfern.

1925. Asplenium Filix-fœmina
Bernh.
Lady Fern.

1296. Asplenium fontanum Bernh.
Rock Spleenwort.

1297. Asplenium lanceolatum Huds.
Lanceolate Spleenwort.

1298. Asplenium marinum L.
Sea Spleenwort.

1299. Asplenium Trichomanes L.
Common Spleenwort.

1300. Asplenium viride Huds.

Green Spleenwort.

1301. Asplenium Adiantum-
nigrum L.

Black Spleenwort.

1302. Asplenium Ruta-muraria L.

Wall-Rue.

1303. Asplenium germanicum Weiss.

German Spleenwort.

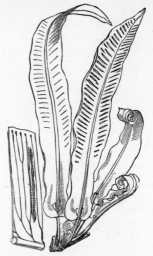

1304. Asplenium septentrionale
Hull.
Forked Spleenwort.

1305. Scolopendrium vulgare
Symons.
Hart's-tongue.

1306. Ceterach officinarum DC.
Rusty-Back.

1307. Blechnum Spicant Roth.
Hard Fern.

1308. Pteris aquilina L.

Brake, Bracken.

1309. Adiantum Capillus-
Veneris L.

Maidenhair.

1310. Cystopteris fragilis Bernh.

Brittle Bladderfern.

1311. Cystopteris montana Link.

Mountain Bladderfern.

1312. Woodsia ilvensis Br.

Alpien W.

1313. Trichomanes radicans Sw.

Bristle Fern.

1314. Hymenophyllum
tunbridgense Sm.

Filmy Fern.

1315. Hymenophyllum
unilaterale Willd.

Filmy Fern.

INDEX.

PRINTED AND BOUND IN GREAT BRITAIN BY WILLIAM CLOWES AND SONS, LIMITED
LONDON AND BECCLES.

WORKS ON THE BRITISH FLORA

Handbook of the British Flora. A description of the Flowering Plants and Ferns, with an Analytical Key to the Families. By G. BENTHAM, F.R.S. Revised by Sir J. D. HOOKER, C.B., F.R.S., and A. B. RENDLE, M.A., D.Sc., F.R.S. 17s. 6d. net.

Illustrations of the British Flora. Drawn by W. H. FITCH, F.L.S., and W. G. SMITH, F.L.S., and others. 1321 Wood Engravings. Revised Edition. 17s. 6d. net.

Further Illustrations of British Plants. By R. W. BUTCHER, B.Sc., F.L.S., and F. E. STRUDWICK, Nat. Sc. Tripos (Cantab.), M.A. (Dublin). Forming a more complete British Flora together with Bentham's Handbook and illustrations. 485 new figures with descriptions. Crown 8vo. Price 17s. 6d. net.

A Students' Illustrated Irish Flora. Being a guide to the Indigenous Seed-Plants of Ireland. By J. ADAMS, M.A. (Cantab.), Economic Botanist, Ottawa, Canada. Illustration and particulars of distribution of each Topographical Distribution. Lists of Poisonous Plants and Lists of English and Irish Names. Crown 8vo. pp. viii+343. 578 Illustrations and Outline Map of Ireland. Price 17s. 6d. net.

The Dispersal of Plants Throughout the World. By HENRY N. RIDLEY, M.A., C.M.G., F.R.S., F.L.S. Showing the means and methods by which plants are distributed throughout the World, by Wind, Water, Animals, Birds, Simple Adhesion, Special Modification, etc., etc. Royal 8vo., pp. 774+xx. With 22 Coloured and half-tone Illustrations. Price £3 3s. net.

The Potamogetons (Pondweeds) of the British Isles; Descriptions of all the Species, Varieties and Hybrids. By ALFRED FRYER, A.L.S., completed by A. BENNETT, A.L.S. With 60 Plates by ROBERT MORGAN, F.L.S., and Miss M. SMITH. Royal 4to. Coloured, £6 6s. net; uncoloured, £4 4s. net.

The Hepaticæ of the British Isles; being Figures and Descriptions of all known British Species By WILLIAM HENRY PEARSON. Complete in 2 Vols. With 228 Plates, each containing from 10 to 15 figures of structural detail. Coloured, £8 8s. net; plain, £4 10s. net.

L. REEVE & CO., LTD., BANK ST., ASHFORD, KENT.

Phycologia Britannica; or, History of British Seaweeds. Containing Coloured Figures, Generic and Specific Characters, Synonyms and Descriptions of all the Species of Algæ inhabiting the Shores of the British Islands. By Dr. W. H. HARVEY, F.R.S. 4 Vols. 360 Coloured Plates. £8 8s. *net*.

L. REEVE & CO., LTD., BANK ST., ASHFORD, KENT.